The King's Flax

and the Queen's Linen

The King's Flax

and the Queen's Linen

Antony G. Searle
&
James W. Tuck

The Larks Press

Published by the Larks Press
Ordnance Farmhouse, Guist Bottom,
Dereham NR20 5PF
Tel./Fax. 01328 829207

Printed by the Lanceni Press,
Garrood Drive, Fakenham.

Cover: Flax in flower, photo by J.W. Tuck

British Library Cataloguing-in-Publication Data
A catalogue for this book is available at the British Library

ISBN 0 948400 78 1

Foreword

Undoubtedly, the trigger for writing a book on the remarkable story of Royal involvement in Norfolk flax was the publication on June 10th 1993 of a mystery photograph in the *Mercury*, an ephemeral free paper circulating in King's Lynn and district. This picture showed some disused factory buildings and the paper asked if anyone could recognise them. Jim Tuck, glancing through the *Mercury*, came across the photo, thought the site looked familiar, then realised it must be the Flax Factory at West Newton on the Royal Estate, which he had known very well forty-odd years before, when he worked in H. M. Norfolk Flax Establishment, of which it was part. His letter describing the place and its past appeared in the *Mercury* for June 24th and ended as follows:- 'This has prompted me into thinking that there is the basis of a worthwhile history to be written here. Any suggestions?' There were none locally. That would have been the end of the matter if one John Frost had not read Jim's letter and remembered that his friend John Matthews (like himself a former teacher at West Walton School, near Wisbech) was connected through his late father-in-law, Gilbert Searle, with Norfolk flax. So he sent the letter off to John and his wife Beatrice ('B.'), now living in Kent. B. decided that it ought to go to her brother Tony Searle in Abingdon, as he had inherited lots of stuff on the 'Norfolk Flax Experiment'. On it went, therefore, to Tony, who wholeheartedly agreed that this flaxen saga should indeed see the light of day. So, through chance and altruistic perspicacity, Jim's query was answered at last with a resounding Yes! The two of us agreed to make *The King's Flax* a joint project, with the history, over many millennia, of flax and linen woven into the fabric. This book is the result.

Many people willingly helped us in our task. First, we should like to thank Her Majesty Queen Elizabeth II for graciously permitting us to make use of material from the Royal Archives at Windsor Castle. Miss Pamela Clark of the Royal Archives, Mrs Brenda Collins and Elaine Flanigan of the Irish Linen Centre in Lisburn, Staff at the Textile Institute, Manchester, as well as Mr J. Major of the Sandringham Estate Office have all provided useful information and helped in various other ways. We should also like warmly to thank several former workers in H. M. Norfolk Flax Establishment who almost brought it back to life by their vivid reminiscences, tape-recorded by Jim. These were Mrs Dorothy Angel (née Galt), Mrs Stella Green (née Booth), Bernard Green and George Smith. Mrs Joyce Griffiths (née Drewry), member of the Office Staff for nearly fifteen years, kindly provided us with her own fascinating and detailed recollections, as well as a comprehensive Staff list for war and post-war years. David Gilling, former member of the Scientific Staff, has read the whole work and made some valuable comments, as well as giving us his own account of the Norfolk flax enterprise and suggesting a suitable publisher for our production. Others who provided information and/or material were Mrs K. M. Cove, Dr R. A. E. Galley, Mrs V. Peacock and Mrs J. Woods. Tony much appreciates the help he has received from his sister, Mrs B. M. Matthews (née Beatrice Searle) in providing fascinating paternal letters and reminiscences, as well as plenty of encouragement from her husband John and herself. Nor should we forget our wives, Susi and Jean, who have shown patience and forbearance with us in our frequently exasperating task. All the help that Susan Yaxley has given us in preparing this book for publication is much appreciated too. We thank them all and anyone else we have inadvertently failed to mention.

Many of the illustrations are from Gilbert Searle's or our own collections. For the rest, we are grateful to the following for permission to use copyright material:-

The Dean & Canons of St George's Chapel, Windsor, page 12
Eastern Daily Press, page 59
The Hulton Getty Picture Collection, pages 4 and 71
Irish Linen Centre, pages 21 and 52
Lynn News and Advertiser pages 55, 71, 88, 89 (top), 90, 92, 93

Finally we wish to dedicate this work to the memory of
GILBERT ODELL SEARLE, whose enthusiasm, dedication and
powers of persuasion ensured that the 'Norfolk Flax Experiment'
blossomed into a nationwide enterprise which helped to defeat one of
the greatest menaces this country has ever had to face.

Tony Searle
Jim Tuck

CONTENTS

N.B. Chapters with personal reminiscences have the author's initials
after the title.

Introduction

The story of the King's Flax, which made an important contribution to victory in the last war, has waited a long time to be told. The King concerned was George the Fifth and the flax was that grown on his Norfolk estate from the early 1930s.

It seemed to be always the King's flax which made newspaper headlines, not his many other crops. Clearly, there was something newsworthy about his decision to grow flax at Sandringham through the years of the economic depression to the last years of his reign. In these pages we explain the background to that decision and its repercussions a few years later when, in 1939, Britain found herself involved in all-out war.

It is not as if the King just grew a few acres of flax and then lost interest; he continued to grow it as long as he lived and encouraged his tenants to do likewise. Moreover, he even allowed a flax factory to be built on his own land at West Newton, and a national centre for flax research to be developed at Flitcham on the Royal Estate which would become a nerve-centre for the flax operation during the war and for many years afterwards. 'The King's persistence in this field'[1] had, in fact, beneficial consequences for the whole country.

People may well ask, what is so special about flax? Its Latin name, given by Linnaeus[2], gives a clue: *Linum usitatissimum*. The adjective means 'most useful'; few if any plants deserve it more. Here we shall concentrate on the variety of flax plant which is grown for its fibre, but that grown chiefly for its seed (linseed) is another variety of the same species and equally useful. The fields of ethereal blue seen in Britain from June-July come mainly from linseed in flower, but recently some flax for fibre has been grown once more[3]. Flax fibre is spun and woven into a wide range of fine linen fabrics, from damask tablecloths through garments of all sorts to sheets and pocket handkerchiefs. Because of its great strength and durability many coarser fabrics are also made of flax, for example canvases, webbing, harnesses and hosepipes, as well as thread, twine and the strongest of ropes. Lint for wound dressing is made from linen cloth. The sails of Nelson's *Victory* were made of it, the famous Bayeux tapestry was embroidered on it and, over two thousand years ago, the precious Dead Sea scrolls were wrapped in linen. Short fibres not suitable for spinning (tow or flax rug) can be converted into high-grade stationery or cigarette paper, or used as packing material. The woody waste from flax, known as 'shive' or 'shives', has been used for polishing tin-plate, making chipboard or as a fuel, while flax chaff is a useful stock feed, especially for sheep. Even flax dust can be a filler for artificial manure and contains a potentially valuable wax.

The uses of linseed are also legion. The seeds are very rich in oil (30-40%), which is used as a wood preservative (especially for cricket-bats!) and in making paints and varnishes, printing inks, linoleum, oilcloths, soaps etc. It has also been used as a coating on roads to prevent surface deterioration. The oil-cake or linseed meal left after oil extraction is rich in proteins. It was eaten by the ancient Greeks and Romans and the best quality is still eaten today, mainly in health foods. The rest is mainly fed to livestock, especially cattle. It can also be used as a poultice. In fact, there are many medical uses, some a bit dubious. Thus *Gerard's Herball*[3] states that 'the seeds stamped with the roots of wild Cucumbers, draweth forth splinters, thornes, broken bones, or any other thing fixed in any part of the body.' Some other remedies seem more believable, for instance the use of seed infusions as mucilaginous drinks to deal with diarrhoea and other signs of gut irritation, as well as diseases of the bladder, or linseed oil used as an ingredient in Carron oil, for the treatment of burns and scalds. The oil has soothing and lubricating properties, which have been used to relieve coughs, sore throats and even tonsillitis. Indeed, a cornucopia of good things cascades from this slender plant!

In our opinion, linen has never been deposed from the proud position it has held for thousands of years as the queen of textiles and the textile of Queens. The King's flax was also the Queen's flax and two Queens were delighted to receive a range of linen articles made from Sandringham's flax. No other vegetable fibre can surpass linen for strength, durability and beauty, while artificial fibres, though extremely useful, are really in a separate category. So it is sad that the words 'linen' and 'linens', flourish more than the textile itself. Although the *Concise Oxford Dictionary* makes it clear that 'linen' means 'cloth woven from flax', one comes across such incredible statements as 'Our crisp and fresh bedroom linen comes in high quality, pure white cotton'![4] Stores have whole departments devoted to 'Household Linens', but these may not contain a single article which is actually made of linen. Somehow, unlike champagne (another quality product), linen seems unable to protect its good name. Let us hope there is still time to reverse this trend!

This book has two main aims: first to describe the fascinating consequences of a King's decision to grow a neglected crop and, second, to give the reader some inkling of the ups and downs experienced by what has been called 'nature's miracle fabric'[5] over the last ten thousand years or so. Linen has been down but it is certainly not out. In fact it shows signs of a renaissance which we hope this book will encourage.

King George V with his favourite pony - without him the Norfolk Flax Experiment might never have taken off
(Hulton Getty Collection)

Chapter 1. Linen: the fabric of history

Human use of the flax plant to make a strong and durable fabric goes back to the dawn of history: one could almost say to Adam and Eve. Witness the couplet coined at the time of the Peasants' Revolt in 1381 which asks 'When Adam delved and Eve span, who was then the gentleman?' The idea that spinning came in with our earliest ancestors is depicted already in the 12th Century on a marble font at All Saints Church in East Meon, Hampshire, where the disgraced pair are shown leaving the Garden of Eden[1]. Eve stalks away, plying her distaff and spindle, while downcast Adam follows with a spade. Admittedly, Eve's distaff looks more suitable for spinning wool but the spinning of flax was even more ancient.

Old font at East Meon showing Eve with distaff and spindle

Whatever its true origins, we can be sure that linen has been made from flax for at least 7,000, perhaps even 10,000 years[2]. A fragment of linen has been found in an Egyptian Neolithic site at Fayum which dates from 5000 BC[3]. Moreover, the world's oldest dress still in existence was made of linen in the first Egyptian Dynasty nearly 5000 years ago[4]. No other natural fabric has lasted, or could last, anything like as long. Also remarkable is the fact that the earliest linen samples were not the rough pieces of fabric one might expect but had a fineness of weave which was almost up to present-day standards. Many centuries must have been needed to advance the methods of linen production from their crude beginnings to this level of sophistication. From the

1st Dynasty Egyptian linen

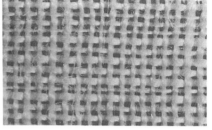

Irish Sheer Linen

dawn of history, flax fibre has also been used as a rope or cord for fishing lines, nets etc., since remains of this material have been found in Stone Age lake dwellings from Switzerland[2].

Hand-pulling the crop in ancient Egypt

Ancient illustrations[5] show how the processes used by the Egyptians to make linen from flax 5,000 years ago are much the same as those of today. The flax crop was harvested by pulling, not cutting, so that the whole length of fibres was kept intact. It was then 'retted' (i.e. rotted) as it is today in tanks of warm water, in order to loosen the fibre from its woody surroundings. After drying, the non-fibrous material was combed out by the process known as 'scutching' or 'swingling', which is done by machine nowadays. The cleaned fibre lengths, or 'rove', was than wet-spun, being passed through a trough of treated water and then drawn out and twisted into a yarn. The Egyptians added a mystery ingredient to the water, but the idea of wet-spinning was re-invented by a Frenchman in 1814. It was thought a most revolutionary advance! Only in weaving did the Egyptians lag a long way behind modern technology, since they did not use any sort of shuttle to combine

Deseeding

6

weft threads with warp. However, they still managed to produce some fine linen cloth. Their linen industry must have been vast, since all people of importance, as well as sacred cats, crocodiles etc., were embalmed and wrapped in linen to form mummies. Sometimes the mummy wrappings (often derived from cast-off garments) extended to 300 yards of various widths, from a few inches to three feet. Those from the famous tomb of Tutankhamun are still in first-class condition, as are a number of the boy-king's garments[3]

Breaking and scutching the retted flax

Linen had many other uses in Ancient Egypt besides wrapping embalmed corpses. For instance, fine linen was the only fabric which could be used by temple priests in the service of Isis, Osiris and other gods. Ceremonial dresses were very ornate and often their material was so fine as to be diaphanous. Linen garments were esteemed above all others by the aristocracy of that time. Linen was also used as a base for embroidery, carpet-making and appliqué work. In addition, ropes made from flax fibres were the strongest of all and were needed to move enormous stone blocks in building the Pyramids. From the earliest times stems of the flax plant were also used for basketry. With so many uses, perhaps it is not surprising that, according to recent findings[6], the earliest examples of true writing, from about 5,300 years ago, are records of linen and oil deliveries to King Scorpion I of Egypt.

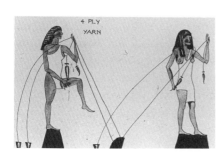

Spinning the fibre

By 3,000 BC flax crops must have been widespread in Mesopotamia as well as the Nile Valley. The Old Testament has many references to the use of linen. Thus the children of Israel 'made coats of fine linen of woven work for Aaron and for his sons, and a mitre of fine linen and goodly bonnets of fine linen, and linen breeches of fine twined linen, and a girdle of fine twined linen, and blue, and purple, and scarlet, of needlework; as the Lord commanded Moses.'[7] Clearly, the use of linen garments by the

7

priesthood was sanctioned by the highest authority. In Proverbs[8] all the qualities of a virtuous woman are listed. For instance, 'she seeketh wool and flax and worketh willingly with herhands....

Weaving

..She layeth her hands to the spindle and her hands hold the distaff.... She maketh fine linen, and selleth it; and delivereth girdles unto the merchant... Her children rise up and call her blessed; her husband also, and he praiseth her.' No wonder! In the New Testament too, St. Mark[9] describes how Joseph of Arimathaea 'bought fine linen and took him (Jesus) down and wrapped him in the linen and laid him in a sepulchre..' Thus started the legend of the Turin shroud. The prophet Muhammad, who died in 632, was reputed to have a linen tunic, painted with gold, which was also believed to have survived through the centuries.

From the Middle East, linen manufacture spread throughout the civilised world, especially to Greece and Rome, where 'purple and fine linen' were prized. Cotton had made its first appearance in India in about 3,000 BC but was looked down on in the West, with 'purple and fine cotton' non-existent. Herodotus wrote in the 5th century BC that wool was ceremonially unclean to the Egyptians, but we now know[3] that it was much used in that country (especially for warm clothing it seems) from the Predynastic period onwards. The Roman author Apuleius (of *Golden Ass* fame) wrote: 'Wool, the excretion of a sluggish body taken from a sheep, is deemed a profane attire, but flax, that cleanest production of the field, is rightly used for the innermost clothing of men', but perhaps he too found wool useful in winter.

Little is known about how the flax industry fared in the Dark Ages but it certainly flourished in Europe in mediaeval times. For instance, there were 40,000 weavers of flax and wool in the Belgian town of Ghent in the 15th century and some very fine pieces of linen were produced. Linen was used as a foundation for coronation and processional robes, some of which survived for hundreds of years. For example, the 12th century coronation robe of Saint Stephan of Hungary was used for the same purpose in the 19th century by the Austro-Hungarian Emperor Franz Joseph[5].

Chapter 2. Flax in Britain

When the blue flowers of flax first adorned British fields is still far from certain. Some think it was introduced by our Roman invaders nearly two thousand years ago. Indeed, spindle whorls made of baked clay or stone have been recovered from a Romano-British site in Norfolk. It may have reached Ireland even earlier, perhaps during the Bronze Age, over 4000 years ago. Possibly it was not cultivated widely at the time of the Norman Conquest, as it is not mentioned among the tithable produce of that period, i.e. subject to a tax of one-tenth its value, payable to the church. Perhaps this was because growing flax, then separating and spinning its fibre, was very much a home industry. By 1175, however, it was classed among the tithable products[1]. The word 'distaff' to describe the stick holding the fibre (flax or wool) to be home-spun, is peculiarly English and Old English at that (i.e. used before AD 1150 or so) while 'spinster' in its original sense was used already in *Piers Plowman* (14th Century) and became the legal designation of an unmarried woman only later. This secondary meaning, and the use of

King Sardanapalus joins the ladies
(From the Ms. of Valerius Maximus)

9

the phrase 'on the distaff side' to describe female members of a family (from the 16th Century on), shows how widespread spinning was as a domestic female occupation. Just occasionally, men would join their female companions in this healthy pursuit: an ancient illustration shows that Sardanapalus, the last king of Nineveh, was not too proud to join the ladies in this way. Geoffrey Chaucer called spinning one of the three resources of women, the other two being weeping and deceit. After such a cheeky remark, I should imagine that some affronted spinster may have used the distaff on him! Its other name was 'rock' (from Old Dutch) and it could easily be turned into a cudgel, as in the following old rhyme:-

'Hands off, with gentle warning,
Lest I you knock with Nancy's rock
And teach you a little learning.'

While spinning was done by the womenfolk, weaving was usually carried out by the men. It used to be a domestic industry too, with thousands of small looms scattered across the countryside. This was especially so in Ireland, where the concentration on spinning and weaving in the 18th Century seems to have had an adverse effect on agriculture in general. Thus Arthur Young[2] wrote at that time: 'View the North of Ireland and you behold a whole province peopled by weavers, it is they who cultivate, or rather beggar, the soil as well as work the looms. Agriculture is there in ruins...' Thanks to the efforts of Louis Crommelin, who did so much (under the patronage of William III) to encourage the flax industry, conditions slowly improved, but the weavers remained steeped in poverty. Thus, in an *Account of Ireland* published in 1808, it is stated that the food consumed by a weaver's family of six cost 5 shillings a week, and consisted almost entirely of potatoes, buttermilk and herrings. No wonder the Irish Potato Famine had such a devastating effect.

Something more should be written about Louis Crommelin, since the story of this remarkable man helps to explain why the flax industry is still so important in Northern Ireland, and why the town of Lisburn (second only to Belfast in population) is particularly associated with this industry, and with its revival in Great Britain[3]. The Crommelin family belonged to the French Protestant community known as Huguenots who, through hard work and shrewdness, had become one of the most prosperous groups in France. The Crommelins themselves were land-owners and flax-growers. Huguenot liberties and religious rights had long been established, most notably by the Edict of Nantes. However, King Louis XIV and his equally bigoted Queen and former mistress, Madam de Maintenon, revoked these and started to persecute the French Huguenots, trying to force them to change their religion. Many managed to escape to neighbouring countries. Among these was the Crommelin family, who settled in Holland and set up a banking business there with the help of money they had smuggled out of France. Among their clients, to whom Louis Crommelin and his brothers used to lend money, was the young Prince William. He was effectively the head of the Dutch Republic and ruler of the small, then independent, state of Orange, situated near Avignon in the south of France. He had married Princess Mary, eldest daughter of the Catholic King James II, so, when James was forced to flee from Britain, Parliament invited William of Orange and Mary to take over. This they did, with virtually no resistance. Shortly afterwards, Parliament established a settlement for Huguenot refugees in the old cathedral city of Lisburn. William III wrote personally to Louis Crommelin to invite him over to advise on the prospects for the Irish linen industry,which at that time was in a primitive state. He settled in Lisburn, made a thorough examination and then reported back on what needed to be done. As a result, he was appointed Overseer of the Royal Linen Manufacture of Ireland. Although the King was determined to encourage the Irish flax industry, Treasury funds had been exhausted by foreign wars. So Crommelin himself had to lend the necessary money, at 8% interest! He then proceeded to buy hundreds of looms from abroad, together with the expertise to use them, and organised a system of technical education in all aspects of flax growing and processing. Thus by the early 18th Century, the linen industry in Ulster had been set on a firm footing. and Britain had become much less dependent on the weavers of France and the Low Countries for her fine linens and sail-cloth. All this enterprise started in Lisburn, so it is not surprising that the Linen Industry Research Association's headquarters (of which we shall read more anon) were near there and that it is home to the Irish Linen Centre.

There seems little doubt that flax flourished in England in the late Middle Ages and that East Anglia was known to be good for its growth. In 1552, for example, Norwich and other towns in Norfolk had, by Act of Parliament, the monopoly for the manufacture of all diaper linens in the Kingdom, i.e. linens with a small diamond pattern. Various Acts of Parliament were passed to encourage the growth of flax and hemp; in fact it was compulsory at one time to include these crops in what was grown by the farmer. Subsidies for flax and hemp-growing only ended in 1836 [4]. Another clue to the importance of these crops is found in St. George's Chapel, Windsor and concerns Sir Reginald Bray, a member of Henry VI's Privy Council and Henry VII's High Treasurer, who died in 1503. He helped greatly in completion of the chapel and added a chantry in the south transept. He took as his badge a brake, a simple device used to break up the outer coating of the hemp or flax stem so that the fibre could be extracted. As a result, the brake is displayed no less than 175 times in the Chapel, sometimes surrounded by the Garter, as he was a Knight of that venerable Order [5]. Perhaps he invented the brake, made a fortune from it and so used it as a badge. However, it seems much more likely that his fortune stemmed from his Royal connections.

The Badge of Sir Reginald Bray in St George's Chapel, Windsor

This brings us on to another link between the processing of flax and the Royal Borough of Windsor, which is also the first example we know of Royal encouragement for the flax industry. Those concerned were Queen Charlotte, wife of George III, and her daughters the Princesses Augusta and Elizabeth, who set up a flax mill at Clay Farm, Old Windsor, in 1817 [6]. The catalyst for this Royal enterprise seems to have been William Bundy's invention in 1817 of a workable scutching machine, as distinct from a primitive brake. Bundy was sure his

12

invention would revolutionize the flax industry, leading to the employment of no less than 781,622 persons in it. Needless to say, it did *not*. This failure may have been connected with a great increase in the use of cotton, imported from the newly independent American colonies.

Another good example of Royal encouragement for the flax industry concerns the Royal Society for the Promotion and Improvement of the Growth of Flax in Ireland, founded in 1841. Queen Victoria and the Prince Consort showed their great interest in it by becoming Patrons and visiting Belfast in 1849 to see a 'marvellous display' by the Society, laid out in twelve rooms, which showed every stage of flax-processing from the raw material to the finished product. The Queen was presented with fine specimens of linen fabrics and it is said that Prince Albert's ideas for the Great Exhibition of 1851 in London were conceived at this show in Belfast[6]. Apparently the Queen and her husband were discussing the impressive flax exhibit as the Royal Yacht took them back across the Irish Sea. A daring Lady-in-waiting broke in to ask the Prince Consort: 'Why can't we have an exhibition in London, Sir?' 'Yes' replied the Prince 'and it shall be an international one!'[7] Eighty-one years later, their grandson King George and Queen Mary visited a similar display at the Science Museum, London and seemed to be equally impressed, judging from subsequent events.

Chapter 3. Flax in East Anglia

Flax continued to be cultivated on a small scale in Great Britain and Ireland in the early 19th century but with so little care and attention that the flax fibre produced was of inferior quality. All the finer material was imported, mainly from Belgium, where there was a first-rate centre for flax production at Courtrai, beside the river Lys, in which the flax was retted. In the 1840s, however, a vigorous attempt was made to revive the cultivation of flax both for fine fibre and for linseed, which was an excellent cattle food. It was known that both could be produced successfully in Britain, yet millions of pounds were spent each year in their import. First, the Flax Improvement Society of Ireland was formed in about 1840. This engaged first-rate Belgian instructors to teach the best methods of culture and after-management of the crop and had a reciprocal arrangement to send young men over to Belgium for training.

River retting on the Lys

This scheme worked very well and the idea was taken up in Norfolk, thanks to the enterprise and enthusiasm of one John Warnes, a remarkable farmer and writer from Trimingham, near North Walsham[1]. He had shown that flax of high quality could be grown in Norfolk, both for fibre and for linseed. He was very distressed at the appalling poverty in which most of his fellow citizens lived and he thought it disgraceful that so much money left

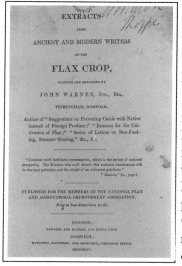

the country to pay for flax products which could be produced here equally well. If this was done it would be 'highly remunerative to the Farmer' and would give 'more varied employment and multiplied benefits than any other production of the earth. The poverty would be relieved by very widespread and useful employment, which would be for a permanency; because as linen ever has been one of the most useful and favourite articles of wearing apparel, so will it continue to the end of time.' Perhaps that view was optimistic but he persuaded the North Walsham Farmer's Club to pass a resolution at their meeting in 1842:- 'That as the soil and climate of England are highly suitable for the growth of flax, it is resolved that a Society shall be formed to promote the cultivation of that important plant in Norfolk, having for its object the advancement of Agriculture, and the finding (of)employment for the poor'.

In this way the Norfolk Flax Society was set up, with the support of the landed gentry, the clergy and the farmers themselves. The first Annual General Meeting of the Society was held in January 1843 in St Andrew's Hall, Norwich, and seems to have attracted 'many of the first gentlemen in the county', from the Lord Lieutenant and High Sheriff to the Lord Bishop of Norwich and The Mayor. In November of the same year a National Flax and Agricultural Improvement Association was formed with Lord Rendlesham as President and John Warnes himself as the Hon. Secretary, to promote the cultivation of flax both for fibre and linseed production. The latter was emphasised because it had been 'incontestably proved that a compound of flax-seed, with grain, pulse or chaff for fattening cattle, is far superior to foreign oil cake and.....will enable every farmer in Great Britain to fatten more than double his number of stock, and render him for ever independent of foreign aid, both for food for his cattle and manure for his land.' Such hyperbole has indeed always been around. The ladies were

15

also invited to support the Association, so that they could introduce the spinning and weaving of linen yarn into 'Schools, Orphan asylums, Magdalen and other institutions where employment is required', especially the sort of fine yarn which 'a woman can spin twenty or thirty shillings worth of...from sixpenny worth of flax.' (Magdalen institutions were homes for reformed prostitutes.)

Clearly, the redoubtable John Warnes generated terrific enthusiasm in favour of a vast increase in flax and linseed growing in Norfolk and indeed in the whole of Great Britain, but the evidence (admittedly meagre) suggests that this did not last for long. Probably this was just due to inertia, a reluctance to switch to an unfamiliar crop which had to be treated in quite a different way from the familiar cereals. The flax crop would have to be retted and scutched; perhaps, to many farmers, it was far from clear where this would be carried out. Positive action was needed to set the whole scheme in motion on a sufficiently large scale, but maybe the incentives for such action were just not enough.

Twenty years later, however, incentives were clear-cut and quite sufficient to cause thousands of acres of flax to be grown and processed in Norfolk. No less than 320,000 acres were grown in the British Isles as a whole in 1864[2]. The root cause was the American Civil War, which stopped the normally massive imports of cotton goods into Britain from across the Atlantic. Linen was the obvious, and superior, substitute and large flax mills were set up near the Millfleet in King's Lynn (the Boal Mill) and in Downham Market. The flax was grown in the fenland area of Norfolk and Cambridgeshire, then brought to the mills in barges. There it was deseeded mechanically, retted in warm water, water-mangled and dried. In the scutch mill it was passed through breaking rollers but was then hand-scutched, since scutching turbines were not yet invented. In other respects the methods used were essentially the same as those of about a century later. The scutched flax was sold to spinners, but the tow (shorter, coarser lengths of fibre) was turned into ropes and twine at the mill.

After 1870 and the return to normality of American cotton imports, this Norfolk flax enterprise rapidly faded away and very little was grown in Great Britain for the next forty years. Then came the Great War (1914-18), when flax became a raw material of national importance. The Army and Navy demanded strong canvases, the Royal Flying Corps (predecessor to the RAF) needed vast areas of aeroplane linen to cover the wings and fuselage. Yet most supplies came from Belgium, Holland and Russia, so they could be cut off, with disastrous consequences, despite Britain's command of the seas. For the first years of the war the linen industry relied on its usual sources. Then, in 1917, the Russian Revolution caused all their flax exports to stop abruptly. As a result there was a serious shortage of seed[3]. Flax production in England and Scotland had to be resuscitated as quickly as possible. 12,000 acres of flax were grown in 1918 and another 12,000 in 1919, but the cost was immense. There were no pulling machines and the harvest was very wet. Some of the harvest camps of inexperienced city workers averaged as much as 150 man-days of work per acre of flax pulled! By a great effort, 13 mills were partly equipped for processing flax, with other smaller ones for deseeding. A fair proportion of the crops were deseeded but hardly any fibre had been produced by the end of 1919, by which time continental flax production was back to normal. The Government then sold the mills but the price of flax fell disastrously in 1920, so the companies concerned had ceased to exist by 1924. Flax growing continued for a time in Somerset with help from the Ministry of Agriculture, who took over some flax mills to process the crop, but once these factories were closed down in 1930 the Great War flax revival was at an end[4].

It was different in Ireland for, during all this time, its flax industry kept going along time-honoured peasant industry lines, with only a few abortive attempts at flax factory development, although there were small scutching mills. This simple scheme had the great advantage that the extent of flax production could easily be adjusted in line with prices and demand, while centralised flax factories could only survive when regional production remained at a fairly high level. Moreover, the methods used to process the flax were expensive and rather primitive, with no technical advances having been made since the last flax revival in the 1860s. It is not really surprising, therefore, that by the time the 1930s Depression started to blight trade and spread unemployment through the western world, flax-growing in Britain (though not in N. Ireland) was a thing of the past. However, this moribund state did not last for long and the fascinating story of its revival by King George V is the subject of this book.

Chapter 4. Flax research: the Ulster initiative

King George V's interest in the idea of growing flax on his own estate moved to decisive action in 1931, when three acres at Sandringham were sown with pedigree flax seed. The story behind these ideas and this decision is inextricably linked with the work of the Linen Industry Research Association (LIRA), based at Glenmore House, Lambeg, Lisburn, Northern Ireland. Knowing something about this organization helps us to understand its role in the revival of flax-growing in Britain.

Like many other research associations LIRA was a direct result of the Great War. As a leading Ulsterman, Sir Edward Carson, wrote at the end of the war:- 'The supreme importance of organisation and science was recognised in Germany far more than by ourselves before the war....Happily, when the need became pressing the British nation proved itself more than equal to Germany in capacity both for organisation and for applied science[1].' Already during the war the Government had realised the danger that after it was all over British industries would regress into slipshod unorganised ways instead of continuing the scientific methods which had proved so valuable. Accordingly, it set up a Committee of the Privy Council for Scientific and Industrial Research, with the task of persuading a large number of industries to set up research associations for the benefit of the whole industry, with initial financial assistance from the Government. The need for intensive research in the linen industry was only too obvious. Many of the methods of processing the flax crop had changed little in hundreds of years and practically no scientific selection had been practised on the flax plant itself, to improve its fibre content and other desirable characteristics. Moreover, Britain imported vast quantities of flax from overseas although there was plenty of evidence that it could grow all it needed, since there were times in the past when it had done just that. The war experience showed only too clearly that the British linen industry should never again be dependent for its main supply of raw material on outside sources. If flax yields could be increased and the cost of linen production could be reduced then there would be less competition from abroad and greater incentives for the home farmer to grow it.

A Provisional Research Committee was set up during the war, to start the ball rolling. It appointed an outsider - an energetic American called John C. Curtiss - to study the linen industry and prepare a scheme of research for presentation to potential supporters of the proposed association. Mr Curtiss wasted no time in putting the scheme in motion, especially by writing a masterly, hard-hitting and very persuasive series of articles for publication in the local press, which were then reprinted in book form[1]. In it he pointed out the stupendous amount of waste in the industry, which had a whole range of potentially valuable by-products, from flax bolls and often the seed as well, to the shives and tow from scutching. There was much waste in spinning too. Scientific research could eliminate this waste, mechanise flax-pulling and greatly improve the scutching process. John Curtiss even mentions the possibility that the creasing of linen garments might be reduced or eliminated through research: this is a problem which still needs attention. He criticized the industry for its wasteful methods of marketing too and was not afraid of lambasting the whole country, especially the universities, for its scandalous neglect of science:- 'The whole British system of education seems to be indifferent, not to say contemptuous, towards the importance of science.' Matters have improved somewhat in the last eighty years, but there is still a shortage of scientists at the top in Government and industry.

'We were totally unprepared for war. Are we going to be equally unprepared for peace?' John Curtiss's impassioned words produced the desired effect, for on September 16th, 1919, the Linen Industry Research Association (LIRA) came into existence[2]. Its Irish members represented 88 firms of spinners, weavers, bleachers, dyers, finishers and general manufacturers, while there were 24 Scottish members and one English one. A Council was formed (with Mr J.G. Crawford as Chairman) which then set up no less than twelve committees and sub-committees to deal with every aspect of organization and research. The first essential was to find a home for the new research institute and there they were lucky. Mary Allen (later the Association's Librarian and eventually Mrs

Glenmore House, Lambeg: home of LIRA

G. O. Searle) was Secretary to the Accommodation Sub-committee and (when asked in 1979) well remembered the day it first went to Lambeg to inspect a large property there, called Glenmore House. 'There were about five of us, including Mr J. O. McCleery, a member of the Council. The seller said he knew nothing about the Linen Industry Research Association and would like some money on account. Without more ado Mr McCleery sat down and wrote out a cheque for £7,000...' This would be equivalent to about £150,000 in to-day's money and certainly clinched the deal, since the actual purchase price for the property, which consisted of a 35-roomed Georgian mansion standing close to the main road in 20 acres of land, was £7,500: quite a bargain really, so it is not surprising that the astute Mr McCleery wanted to settle straight away. The place was ideal for its new role as Research Institute, especially because of its fine large well-lit rooms, its spacious outbuildings and extensive grounds, which were very suitable for the experimental plots required for plant breeding work.

In his book on the need for scientific research in the linen industry and its likely results, John Curtiss stressed repeatedly the vital importance of plant selection, to produce pure strains of flax with the superior and uniform qualities needed for linen production.

In this connection the name of Dr J. Vargas Eyre is mentioned more than once as someone who was an expert in this field. From 1911-1915 Dr Eyre and co-workers had been selecting for tall flax varieties, by the use of Livonia and other seed types which he had obtained in Russia in 1911. This work was carried out at two well-known centres for agricultural research: Rothamsted Experimental Station and Wye College, Kent, which was the oldest part of London University. It is not surprising, therefore, that Dr Eyre was chosen in 1919 to be the Association's first Director of Research. Moreover, the first of twenty items listed in the Research Programme for the new Institute was 'The selection and breeding of improved strains of flax seed for sowing purposes.'

As we shall see, this botanical and genetic line of enquiry was particularly successful and led to fibre yields which were much higher than those from non-pedigree stocks. In addition, it was this line of work in particular which became the rationale behind the 'Norfolk flax experiment', which germinated on the Royal estate at Sandringham.

LIRA Staff in 1925 with Dr Vargas Eyre (first Director) in the centre, front row. Mary Allen (Librarian and later Mrs Searle) is beside him on the left and Dr Davin on the far left. Gilbert Searle is behind Miss Allen.

Chapter 5. LIRA: the team at Lambeg. (AGS)

At this stage in the narrative we must introduce an individual who played a leading role in this flaxen adventure, which started in 1919 with LIRA and ended 39 years later with the closure of H.M. Norfolk Flax Establishment. His name was Gilbert Odell Searle, he was my father and one could almost say that he arrived on the scene in a first class railway carriage! This was in 1920 when, completely by chance, he found himself in the same carriage as the LIRA's Research Director, Dr Eyre. Presumably they chatted about this new project for which experienced research workers were required, realised that here was a job which was right up his street and, soon after, was appointed Chief Botanist at Glenmore House. After that lucky break he would often extol the benefits of first class travel.

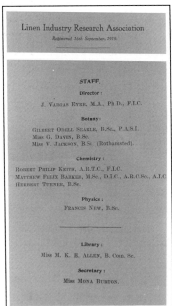

First-footers at LIRA

Gilbert Searle's father and grandfather were architects but he had developed an interest in natural history while a schoolboy at Dulwich College. He had gone on to take a B.Sc. degree in agricultural science at Wye College in 1912, followed by some research work on plant diseases. Then came the Great War. He enlisted as a Private in the Buffs (East Kent Regiment) and ended up unscathed, and married, as a Major in the 12th (Bermondsey) Battalion of the East Surrey Regiment. After the war, he was allowed to retain his rank. He could then resume his postgraduate research on plant diseases, this time at Cambridge University with F.T.Brooks, later to become Professor of Botany there. I don't suppose his research grant was very generous, and already he had a wife, young daughter (Beatrice, born 1917) and baby son (David, born 1920) to support, so it must have been quite a relief to land a fairly senior post when still under 30. Of course he had to move to Northern Ireland but without any house-hunting, since rooms were provided for the family in the original part of Glenmore House. This was because his work would involve much preparation and supervision of outdoor plots for flax-breeding and selection experiments.

In 1921, my father was joined by an Assistant Research Botanist, Adelaide Gladys Davin. This was the start of a most productive partnership, which was to last for over 30 years. Miss Davin had worked previously with Professor Karl Pearson F.R.S., a distinguished mathematician, biometrician and geneticist who held various Chairs at University College London. Miss Davin had been one of his biological assistants in the Biometric Laboratory, with financial help from a Crewdson-Benington studentship. It is clear that Karl Pearson held her in very high regard, since they published three very lengthy and erudite papers together in the scientific journal *Biometrika*[1,2]. The first two[1] were 'On the sesamoids of the knee-joint' (small bones, variable in size and number, found in muscle tendons of hands and feet as well as the knee). The papers included 37 plates, which were mostly drawings of limb-bones presumably by Miss Davin, who was an excellent illustrator. Their third joint paper, 'On the biometric constants of the human skull', is of particular interest [2]. It was based on a collection of 1800 Ancient Egyptian skulls dating from the 26th to 30th dynasties (BC 600- 200) provided by the Egyptologist Sir Flinders Petrie, who also worked at University College London. Many measurements had to be made on each skull by Miss Davin and the other assistants but she alone carried out the statistical analysis, as the following passage from the paper shows: 'More laborious work of tabling and arithmetical reduction was entirely the work of Adelaide G. Davin and was carried on amid frequent interruptions by other duties during the years in which she was biological assistant in the Biometric Laboratory.' Her training in this field, especially in the calculation of correlation coefficients (which measure the relationship between different variables, like height and weight, in a group of individuals and were first introduced into statistical theory by Karl Pearson himself) was exactly what was needed in the plant

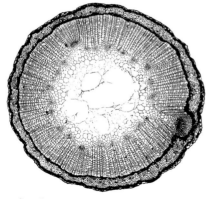

Enlarged cross-section of a flax stem to show fibre bundles round the outside. Each contains many ultimate fibres

selection work on flax. It was because the Davin/Searle team first established correlations between various useful characteristics of the flax plant, such as height and percentage of fibre in the stem, that their subsequent selection work was so efficient and successful.

Miss Davin moved into a cottage just by Glenmore House and the flax-breeding work began. The varieties used at first were some brought from Russia by Dr Eyre and a commercial Dutch one. A series of papers were published as LIRA Memoirs under the general title of 'A botanical study of the flax plant.' Already in 1922 there was one on the use of statistical methods[3], to be followed by a more detailed analysis[4]. The authors described how they cut transverse sections of the stem and made different measurements of the stem and of the fibre bundles inside, as well as counting the number of fibres. They found a number of positive correlations which enabled them to adopt the best selection strategy. Thus there was a high positive correlation between the area of the stem and the total area of fibre bundles within the stem, as well as between the number of fibres and the length of stem, for instance. To obtain both quantity and fineness of fibre it seemed necessary to select for tallness while keeping the thickness of stem constant. However, other factors had to be considered too, such as the ability of the variety to stand up to bad weather. At the same time much breeding work was being carried out to establish which characters of the flax plant were heritable. Flower colour certainly was (white, pink and dark violet flowers were known as well as the usual blue-violet) and the time of flowering, percentage of fibre, and length of the unbranched part of the stem were shown to be so as well.

A cross between a short flax variety (left) with many fibre bundles and a tall one with fewer (right) gave progeny (centre) combining both desirable characters i.e. tallness and high fibre content. Relevant cross-sections of stem are shown below.

With this selection régime it didn't take long before new pure-bred 'Liral' varieties were being produced, with greatly improved characteristics as compared with the commercial non-pedigree strains which were previously available. It has been estimated that the average return of fibre per acre from these Liral varieties was 50% higher than from commercial strains. In other respects, like uniformity and ease of processing, they were also superior. Among the new Liral varieties were Pioneer (the first one, bulked in 1923), Beatall, Duke, Monarch, Crown, Dominion, Purple and Prince. The last was the most successful, being grown extensively (over 2 million acres) all over the world.

In the early 1920s the LIRA scientific staff grew rapidly so that research could be started on other aspects of linen production besides plant-breeding. Thus Drs Cashmore, Kinkead and Mr Henderson worked under Dr Nodder in the Chemistry Laboratory, with Mr New, Miss Wilson and Mr Gregson in Physics, Mary Allen and Hope Preston in the Library and Ethel Hill as the Director's Secretary. Alas, there are no surviving staff from those days to tell us what it was really like to be there and, so far as I know, all the 'Memoirs' which appeared are technical ones, based on the results of research. Yet they had plenty of fun too, as we can see from the contents of a remarkable 'house journal' called 'The Lambeg Lyre'. This appeared once only, at a Fancy Dress Party for the first

Director, given on the eve of his departure in 1925. This aptly named spoof newspaper ('established 4004 B.C.') was my father's brainchild and entirely created by him. We can

picture the scene, as told to me by my stepmother (then Mary Allen, the Librarian) about 60 years after the event. The Fancy Dress Ball was in full swing in the hall of Glenmore House when suddenly this ragged news-boy appeared, dressed in an old suit with a hat over his eyes. Amid general amazement he doubtless called out 'Lambeg Lyre, Lambeg Lyre - read all about it!' as he handed out copies of his scurrilous news-sheet. There must have been more amazement when the assembled company read it and found that they were all in it, in one disguise or another, with their foibles and frailties cunningly lampooned. Thus a revue by the 'Grand Lambeg Palace of Varieties' was advertised. Among the 'All cast stars' was 'The World's Greatest Mimic, Finicky Cashless', i.e. Dr Cashmore, just gone to live in Finaghy. His 'droll entertainment' would include an 'Imitation of Harry Tate in Buying a Car, followed by his own screaming farce just out, "Buying a House"'. My father had noted how often he talked about these. Another star was billed as the 'Eighth Wonder of the World', being HOT HEN, the Human Volcano! 'This man is so hot he has to be stored in an ice chest, and when on view is kept in a constant draught to prevent conflagration.' 'Hot Hen' was really Mr Henderson, another chemist, who never felt cold and was always throwing windows wide open, according to my stepmother. He was an excellent pianist and also features in the Lyre as Mr Hen-Elgar 'who gave a magnificent display of his gifts in that ornate, vulgar and rather Saint-Saenish Pianoforte concerto No.49288 in Z major by Mendeljohn. His trills, twirls, runs, arpeggios, staccatos, pistachios, finishing up with a masterly short arm balance on the lower E and two dropped crotchets brought the audience to its feet in a frenzied uproar.' This was at the 'Lambeg Conservatorium', where 'the whole audience thrilled with emotion and went goosey all over as the sinuous form of Mlle Marie

Allenini (complete with blue sash) wafted itself within their ken. In a moment amidst a silence so profound that you could hear the pickpockets at work, her silvery cadences rang through the encircling gloom, echoed from the rafters and reverberated from the floor in that colourful chromatic and melodic morsel Tosti's "Good-bye" in E flat minimus....' This was Mary Allen, my future stepmother, who was indeed a fine singer. She may have been less pleased with her appearance in the paper's Miscellaneous column: 'WANTED 1 year's supply of stale biscuits for an Institute Tea Club. For Forms of Tender apply:- Miss Mallen, Mental Hospital, Lambeg.', or as 'Mary, Mary (rather contrary)' in the 'Answers' column, who is told that 'Making assignations with boys has to be very carefully done if it is not to be misunderstood...' !

My father, who produced this extraordinary concoction, appears in it as 'Gory O'Spatterblood" (his initials being G.O.S.) who narrates a sanguinary serial about the knavish tricks of 'Don Vargas The Inquisitor' (aka The Director, Dr Vargas Eyre), in which G.O.S. appears again as a 'surly' fellow called 'Sog, The Keeper of the Knives'. His sole joy lay 'in his collection of all sorts and shapes of knives which he spends his days in whetting and polishing.' This refers to the chief activity of the Botanical group: cutting sections of flax plants, for which very sharp instruments were needed. Don Vargas, with the help of his 'familiar' Hew (his Secretary Miss E.W. Hill) and advisers, plans to despoil the rich but 'simple-minded merchants of the land whose chief business is the bartering of linen, a textile material so-called because it is chiefly made from hemp and cotton.'! These merchants were really the supporting members of LIRA, who were supposed to make an annual contribution towards its upkeep.

I had first seen the light of day in Glenmore House about four years earlier (November 1921) and there were two items in the 'Lyre' which were of special interest to me. One was an advertisement by 'Miller and Linol Ltd' about a new adhesive which 'sticks everything and lasts for years... as laid successfully on floors at Lambeg.' I can only have been a toddler, but I have a distinct memory of that sticky linoleum along the corridors at Glenmore House. The other was a Situations Vacant notice, supposedly put in by 'Mrs. Sog, Glenburn Park.':- 'Wanted immediately, General Servant, clean, respectable, honest, small appetite, easy with coals.

Must do family washing, all house work, entire care of four children, two walks daily, clean pram, digging in garden, run errands...In by 9 p.m., up at 5 a.m. Six references. Wages, £6 per year less fines.' I was one of those four children, since 'Mrs Sog' with mammoth expectations was a pseudonym for my mother! Shortly before, the rooms we occupied in Glenmore House had been required for extra laboratory space, so the Searle family had to move to Belfast (Glenburn Park). This meant quite a long journey to work for my father. After the luxury of living on the premises I expect the change was far from welcome.

The new LIRA Director was Dr W. H. Gibson, O.B.E., D.Sc, who lasted thirteen years in the job, until shortly after the outbreak of war in 1939. For the rest of the 1920's much of the Institute's research, apart from the botanical work which we have already discussed, concentrated on finding out more about the chemical constitution of the flax plant and its products, such as flax wax[5], as well as technical studies on the retting process and how it could be improved, and on the sizing process for stiffening fabrics.. It was realised, however, that what was needed more than anything else, was the proper mechanisation of the multitude of processes which led from the flax plant to the linen end-product. These technical aspects received top priority under Dr Gibson's direction, especially the design of machines for pulling and deseeding as well as improved methods of scutching the flax and generally separating the fibres from the rest of the stem as thoroughly as possible before delivery to the mills for spinning and weaving[6]. The primitive and smelly retting process remained a particular problem. In Courtrai, reputed to produce the best flax fibre, they actually retted the crop twice, a very laborious process. Two approaches were tried by LIRA. One was the so-called duplex ret, in which the flax plants were stitched into thin mats (as needed also for other processes like deseeding) and then loaded into the retting tanks. There was then a change of water, before removal of the mats for drying against fences. The other approach was not to ret at all. A 'crimper breaker' was designed which did a very good job of separating the fibres in unretted or 'natural' flax, although the product was more suitable for weaving coarser products, like canvas, than fine linens. It proved invaluable in the war.

Chapter 6. Royal intervention

At the end of the 1920's the future for fibre flax did not look bright. First, there was a national and world-wide economic depression which affected British agriculture as badly as any other industry. Second, there was a general lack of incentive to grow flax in Great Britain because the war-time factories had all closed down, so there was nowhere to send it for processing. It was quite clear, however, that if the flax industry could be started up again in Britain its chances of success were high. It was known that it could be grown without difficulty anywhere in the country and the new Liral strains of pedigree flax could produce fibre yields which were much higher than those from Russian flax, for example. Improved methods of processing the flax were now available; in fact an Experimental Flax Factory had been set up by LIRA at Lambeg, with the aid of grants from the Empire Marketing Board and the Northern Ireland Government. Thus there was no need at all for this country to import so much of its flax, no need for it to use 10 per cent of the world supply but only produce 1 per cent. As Gilbert Searle wrote in 1929:- 'The market for the fibre is available, the best seed in the world is exclusively available. The machinery and methods for extracting the fibre are available. All that is required for success is the organisation of flax factories on up-to-date but not flamboyant lines and the hearty co-operation of the farmer.'[1] All that was needed was someone to start the ball rolling. In fact, the person who did this, and helped greatly to keep it rolling, was King George V himself. It would be difficult to think of anyone else more suited to taking this initiative. He was highly respected and had great influence: if and when he took the lead many others would follow. His estate at Sandringham seemed ideal for this enterprise; it was known already that flax grew well in the lighter soils of Norfolk. Moreover, his interest in the agricultural and economic side of flax-growing was supplemented by Queen Mary's keen interest in its final product: linen. In her School of Needlework on the Sandringham estate this fabric was much used already.

29

It is still unclear when and why the King first decided to grow a trial acreage of pedigree flax at Sandringham in 1931. It has been said that the idea came to him when he, with Queen Mary, visited a large exhibition of flax and linen which was organised by LIRA and held at the Science Museum in London from November 1930 until February 1931. However, the King and Queen only visited the exhibition on February 12th[2]; surely a decision must have been made before then for a sowing that year. This is confirmed by a speech made in London by Mr H. L. McCready, then Chairman of the LIRA Council, at a meeting on 'Post-war problems of the Linen Trade' held on January 22nd 1931. According to *The Times* he 'announced that the King had consented to devote 2 or 3 acres of his estate in Norfolk to the experiment of growing flax of the pedigree varieties bred by the Linen Industry Research Association. This was a further proof of the continued interest which the King took in the industries of his country and the linen trade was hopeful that his very practical action would stimulate the movement for the production by British agriculture of the raw material required by the Irish and Scottish linen industry.'[3] Clearly, someone connected with LIRA had a lot to do with the King's decision. Perhaps it was also connected with the 'prolonged and dangerous illness' which had laid him low not long before.

The King had, in fact, almost died in 1928-9 from a lung infection which turned to septicaemia. In those days before antibiotics this was a very serious condition to be in and the outcome was touch-and-go. 'It was his bloody guts that pulled him through', as one of his Ministers remarked, but he did not recover fully until the end of 1929. He had gone to Sandringham to recuperate in August of that year and also had a spell of convalescence in Bognor. During this period of release from royal routine he would have had more time than usual to think and read about other matters. The long-lasting Depression must have had a serious financial effect on incomes from his estates so that suggestions on how revenues might be increased would not fall on deaf ears. From this point of view the Searle article[1] was very persuasive: no manure needed, no nitrogenous fertilizers, no threshing; rather poor soil gives the best yield of fibre, which is what the factory wants. Fibre values would be up to about £18 per acre, which was quite a lot of money in those days. Moreover the industry 'should and could be wholly British from the sowing of the seed to the sewing of the last stitch in the finished linen goods. It is no upstart new crop...it is an old friend who, after being in business for a modest 7,000 years or so. has now had a good overhaul and is ready, once again, to render tried service to agriculture.' We do not know whether the King saw this particular article, but LIRA must have assured him and his Land Agent, Mr A.C. Beck, that they would help in every way possible, such as supplying the pedigree seed and the expertise. The King pondered, the King consulted, the King decided to 'have a go'.

Having made the momentous decision to grow flax at Sandringham - apparently the only flax to be grown in the whole of England in 1931 - the King and Queen demonstrated their own interest in that crop by visiting the special exhibition at the Science Museum which we mentioned earlier. It was fully reported in *The Times*[4]. This had been opened in style by Lord Parmoor, Lord President of the Council, who pointed out that the linen industry was one of the first to form a trade association. He also talked about the skill of Egyptian craftsmen 7,000 years ago (there were examples of 1st Dynasty linen in the exhibition), about the new strains of pedigree flax being produced with a higher fibre content, the experiments being done on spinning and weaving, the £4000 a year Governmental grant to the Association and said 'He would urge that further assistance was needed.' Clearly he had been well briefed by LIRA whose present and past Directors then followed him in the speech-making before there was a general tour of the exhibition which included over 300 specimens of flax and linen of different ages and different stages in processing. According to *The Times,* 'linen damasks and fine bed-linen monogrammed for the King and Queen drew particular attention.'

That was in November 1930. The King and Queen did not visit LIRA's show until the following February, on returning to London from their winter holiday in Sandringham[3]. They arrived at the Science Museum at 3 p.m. and were received by the Duchess of Abercorn, whose husband was Governor of Northern Ireland at that time. She then presented Lord Craigavon (Prime Minister of NI) and Lady Craigavon to them, as well as Mr Milne Barbour, who was NI Minister of Commerce. The Northern Ireland Government must have attached great importance to this visit,

31

which they hoped would help to stimulate interest in the 'Queen of textiles' and thus boost production for the Ulster spinners and weavers. After all, ship-building and linen manufacture were the two main industries of the province; both were under a cloud and in need of all the help they could get. Queen Mary certainly did her best as they went round. Apparently she 'took particular interest in the finished goods and new damask patterns and enquired where they might be purchased in the London shops.' Among those presented to the King and Queen before they left (after 45 minutes) were members of LIRA Council, including Mr McCready, its Chairman (who had revealed the King's flax-growing intentions three weeks earlier) and Dr Gibson, LIRA Director.

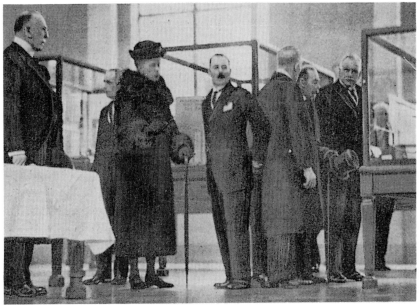

The Times

The King and Queen inspecting exhibits at the Linen Research Exhibition at the Science Museum, South Kensington in 1931 Lord Craigavon is on the left.

Chapter 7   The first Royal crop (AGS)

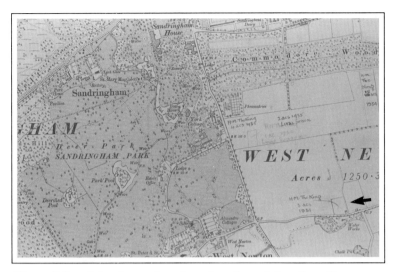

Map of Sandringham showing the site of the first flax crop

We know precisely where on the Royal Estate the first crop of flax was grown because my father recorded on a large-scale map all the sites of all the early sowings. The three acres were, in fact, on Appleton Farm, being just across the West Newton to Flitcham road from Appleton Water Tower. It is a road I used to cycle along regularly on my way from Flitcham Abbey to school in King's Lynn, so I knew the Water Tower very well, from the outside. It is an impressive structure, built in 1877 to supply clean water to Sandringham House and estate and thus get rid of the ever-present threat of typhoid, which killed the Prince Consort and nearly killed the Prince of Wales (later Edward VII). George V was present as a boy of 12 when the foundation stone was laid by his mother, the Princess of Wales, later to become Queen Alexandra. At last, in 1993, I could see the inside of the Water Tower, as it is now leased to the Landmark Trust, which rescues and revives old buildings and makes them fit for human habitation[1]. We booked a short stay there and climbed to the top of the water-tank, from where the site of the original flax field could be seen just a hundred yards away. It was a thrill to realise that, 62 years earlier, my father must have climbed

Appleton Water Tower

up to the very same place in order to photograph that first crop being pulled by hand - a bit of history in the making one could say. The pedigree seed used, partly Liral Crown and partly Liral Monarch, produced an excellent crop which weighed 6 tons (2 tons per acre). There was nowhere to process it in Britain, so it was tied up in large bundles and sent over the sea to Northern Ireland, to be deseeded, retted, scutched etc. at Glenmore House, in LIRA's own experimental plant. This had been set up with the help of grants from the Empire Marketing Board and the Northern Ireland Government, with the main aim of mechanising the laborious hand operations used before in processing flax. This Sandringham crop produced 17 cwt. of scutched flax fibre of excellent quality.

There is one mystery connected with the start of flax-growing at Sandringham, which makes me wonder whether this 3 acre crop

First crop being pulled, viewed from Appleton Water Tower

of 1931 really was the first. In my father's large-scale map which neatly shows in red ink the location, acreage and other details of all

34

these early crops, there is one entry, quite close to the 1931 one, which is not in red ink but only in pencil. It reads: 'HM the King 1 ac 1930 Liral Sussex'. Perhaps this means that, in order to make sure that conditions at Sandringham really were suitable for flax, a very experimental first crop was grown rather secretly a year in advance, as a precautionary measure. After all, it would have been most embarrassing if the three acre crop had been a failure. Alternatively, it might have been hoped to grow a first crop in 1930, but arrangements fell through. That seems less likely, as the location etc. of a hypothetical crop would hardly be entered before it received the green light. Perhaps we will never know the true explanation, unless some reader of this book can enlighten us.

Jimmy Duprey scutching the first crop on a wheel

In any event, it was clear that the 'Norfolk Flax Experiment', as it came to be known, had got off to a good start, with a high yield of fibre which was of fine spinning quality. The next point to be decided was what should be done with this precious Royal product. It didn't take long for LIRA Council, mainly composed as it was of Directors of spinning and weaving firms, to suggest an admirable solution: the flax fibre would be transformed into a variety of useful linen products which would then be presented to their Majesties, if they consented. Indeed they did, and expressed great interest in the flax experiment. Detailed planning then went ahead on all aspects of the presentation, from the range of different

35

linen goods to be produced to the exact dimensions of sheets and design of the Royal monogram to go on them. As Dr Gibson (LIRA Director) remarked at one stage: 'It is like working out a very complicated jigsaw puzzle'. LIRA Council agreed that Wm. Ewart & Sons Ltd (whose Chairman at that time was the same person as their own Chairman, Mr H. L. McCready) would be responsible for spinning the fibre into yarns, while they and nine other firms would prepare the finished goods.

Presentation Day was December 19th 1932 at Buckingham Palace, when a deputation of ten directors of linen firms (nine from Ireland and one from Scotland), together with Dr Gibson and my father, were presented to the King and Queen[2]. Their Majesties were then given the impressive selection of linen goods made from Sandringham flax, whereupon they 'were graciously pleased to express their warm approval of the results obtained and congratulated the Research Association on the success of this valuable piece of work.' It was made clear that much more flax would be grown in Norfolk in 1933. It is fascinating to scan the full inventory of linen goods produced from just three-quarters of a ton of flax fibre:-

1. 1 dozen 4 x 3 yard damask tablecloths, with 12 dozen napkins to match, made by Wm. Ewart & Son. (Mr H. L. McCready)
2. 1 dozen 3¼ yards square damask tablecloths, with 12 dozen napkins to match, made by Hay & Robertson. (Major W. B. Robertson, D.L.)
3. 1 dozen pairs of double sheets, made by the York Street Flax Spinning Co. (Mr William Henry)
4. 2 dozen pillow-cases, made by the Ulster Weaving Co. (Mr J. Graham Larmor)
5. 400 yards of dress linen in various colours, made by Messrs Brookfield Linen. (Mr H. H. Campbell)
6. 250 yards of Slemish furnishing linen, made by the Old Bleach Linens. (Mr N.F. Webb)
7. 24 dozen fine towels and 24 dozen huck (rough) towels, made by Broadway Damask Co. (Mr R. Hetherington), Thos. Ferguson & Co (Mr J. D. Ferguson), Ross Bros. (Mr H. C. Ross) and Webb & Co (Mr W. Henry Webb).

36

The names in brackets are the firms' representatives at the ceremony. Finally, the 2 cwt of tow removed by the scutching was converted into best quality notepaper for use by the Royal Household. It must have lasted them for some time. Note the size of the tablecloths, which must have graced many a banquet on the massive Royal dining-tables. Linen is so durable that many of these items must be still in use. It is good to know that some of the firms are still in business.

Tablecloth made from Sandringham flax 1932

No flax was grown on the Sandringham estate, or elsewhere in Norfolk in 1932, but plenty was done by LIRA to encourage farmers to think about the possibility of growing it, once a local flax factory had been established. For instance, on 27th July the Association mounted a special exhibit on flax and linen at the annual Sandringham Flower Show, a very popular event. This was widely reported, for example by *The Times*[3], which stated that samples of Norfolk-grown flax were exhibited. LIRA produced a leaflet on 'Flax for the Linen Industry', written by my father, for distribution at the exhibition[4]. It pointed out that over 80% of the raw material for the Irish and Scottish linen industries came from Eastern Europe, that much higher yields of fibre could now been obtained from the new pedigree varieties developed by the LIRA and that, thanks to the King, such flax had been grown in Norfolk in a carefully controlled experiment. This had shown that 'a vast proportion of the flax fibre needed for linen could be grown, and in fact could be better grown, in the British Isles particularly in the Eastern Counties....The return to the farmer should vary from £5 to £6.10s.0d per ton...' Norfolk seemed especially suitable for flax cultivation, with an ideal climate and a wide range of soils, so it was hoped to set up a small flax factory in the county, which would lead to the development of a modernised flax industry that would 'spread all up and down the East Coast to the benefit of the farmers in particular and the linen industry as a whole.' In conclusion, interested farmers and landowners were invited to send their names to the LIRA Director of Research in N. Ireland, who would keep them informed of all developments. The key phrase in all this was:-'..it was hoped to set up a small flax factory in the county..' As LIRA realised, this was a vital necessity, as the extra costs of transporting bales of untreated flax to Ireland for processing would eat into profits and discourage farmers from joining the scheme. Although the leaflet only specified Norfolk county as the site for a flax factory, it was realised straight away that the best site of all would be on the Royal estate. To allow construction of a flax factory near Sandringham, with all its consequences (especially perhaps the very dubious smell from retting) was asking a lot more of the King than merely to grow a few acres of flax. Perhaps it was too much...perhaps they hesitated, but not for long. They must have plucked up courage and wisely decided to 'strike while the iron is hot'. Very soon after Royal flax had been exhibited at the Sandringham Flower Show the King was sent 'Proposals for the Establishment of a Flax Industry on the Sandringham Estate', written once again by G.O. Searle and dated August 3rd 1932 [5].

This was a very persuasive document. It began by pointing out that the Irish and Scottish linen industries were 90% dependent on foreign, mainly Russian flax. Its growth in Britain instead would help agriculture and 'aid in rectifying an adverse trade balance.' This could happen if flax and fibre yields were high and of good quality and if the whole process was mechanised. The 1931 experiment, using LIRA's pedigree flax, had given three times the average Soviet yield per acre and a 50% increase in fibre quality. Moreover, LIRA hoped soon to develop 'a perfected scheme of flax fibre production on mechanised lines' which would allow competition on level terms with foreign flax producers. Thus conditions were favourable for further progress towards a successful flax industry through (a) 'construction of a model flax factory in the Eastern counties....with the most up to date plant', (b) building a small research station to continue work on pedigree flax, flax cultivation etc., (c) persuading local landowners to grow up to 600 acres of pedigree flax. They could expect a gross return of £12.10s. to £16.5s. per acre. The Sandringham Estate had particular advantages for such an enterprise. These included the variety of soils (allowing tests of flax growth under different conditions), a similar climate to that in those parts of Belgium which produced the best quality of flax fibre, the possibility of obtaining large acreages of flax under a single control, the central location of the estate in the Eastern Counties and, of course, the kudos accruing to the flax industry if it became associated with the Sandringham Estate. Moreover an 'eminently suitable' site for a model flax factory had already been found, on 60 acres of open flat land (known as the 'rabbit warren') which was 'near the Paper Mill on the Babingley river.' This was on a secondary road, with a good water supply from the river, but was well away from Sandringham House and other residences. This site was marked by my father on his original large-scale map of the estate and was in fact where the flax factory was built a few years later.

Site of the first flax factory on the Royal Estate

These proposals ended with a brief account of financial aspects. If 600 acres of flax were grown each year then the retail value of the linen produced would be about £105,000, of which £9,000 would go to the flax growers. The flax factory would cost under £10,000 to build, with a working capital of about £12,000.

Possibly the factory itself could become the linen merchant, 'with distinct financial advantage to those concerned in its establishment and the assurance to the Royal Households of a continuous supply at wholesale rates of linen of unimpeachable quality and entirely British origin.'

These proposals seem to have had a very favourable reception in Royal circles, though they may have been helped by a mistaken belief that they had been prepared by the King's Land Agent, Mr Beck. Thus Sir Frederick Ponsonby (the King's Treasurer) wrote to him: 'The King has shown me your proposal to grow flax on the Sandringham estate - it reads like a fairy tale - to realise a profit of £12-£16 an acre on 300 acres will suddenly make His Majesty's farms pay.'[6] In actual fact the figure of £12-£16 referred to the gross return; the profit was likely to be about £5 an acre according to my father when he answered a number of questions from the King on financial aspects, marketability, abnormal risks to the flax crop etc. He added that 'If we make sure that each step is based on the results of research here there should be every chance of the factory being profitable...If the first factory were successful the scheme could be extended to a larger scale.'[7]. The exigencies of war made sure that this happened anyway.

The King could not attend the Sandringham Flower Show on July 27th because he was away on the Royal yacht *Victoria and Albert*. However he showed his interest in it, especially in the exhibit of his flax, in two main ways. First, he had press cuttings on the Show (including one from *The Times*, mentioned earlier) sent to him, in which the flax exhibit received a special mention.[8] Second, he sent instructions via Mr Beck that my father should bring the flax exhibit to Sandringham so that he and the Queen could see it on their return. What happened on that occasion was vividly and amusingly described by my father in a letter written the following day to my sister, then aged 15, and the rest of his family. The following are extracts:-

'My dear Beatrice, ...I saw the King and Queen yesterday.... I had my exhibit all ready and it looked very nice; it was at the entrance to the great coach house next to the King's museum where he keeps all his tiger skins and so on. When they were nearly due to come I stood waiting and Mr Beck who was to present me went

40

away for a minute to see if the furniture school was ready for the Queen and of course just as he had gone the King and Queen came walking up all alone. They sailed up to me and the Queen bowed, so I bowed and the King took off his hat and as I hadn't a hat I tried another bow and then we stood and grinned at each other, and I rubbed my nose with one finger and stood first on one leg and then on the other and wished something would happen, but they kept on smiling so I guessed I wasn't going to be beheaded straight away and finally Mr Beck came running up, all puffing and panting, and the King never gave him a chance to present me properly, but inquired my name and at once came forward and shook my hand and said "Good morning Mr Searle, it is very nice of you to bring this exhibit to show us." and the Queen then did likewise and I tried out a few more bows for luck and then everything went very nicely. I got a couple of chairs for them and they sat for a whole hour and never stopped talking once. The Queen was awfully keen on some of my linen, she pounced at once on some special new furnishing linen, sort of tapestry stuff, I had brought and said "Oh George, do come and look at this. It's just what I want and only 8s/11d a yard!" - just like any other housewife would say to her poor husband. And George came and looked and said it was very nice. Then the King talked about flax and said he had read through every word I had written about it, and if I liked he would grow 2000 acres for me and his friend Mr Parker would grow another 2000 acres and that I could have the site for the flax factory on the estate and he quite agreed with the piece I had chosen which was around 70 acres, in fact he gave me everything I wanted but quite overlooked all the difficulties there will be in getting the money to build the factory and pay him for the flax and so on. But I expect we shall manage somehow. Anyway it was all very friendly and he kept on making jokes and I ventured on one or two and managed to make the Queen laugh, but all the time one rather felt it was all because they were so well brought up and had such perfect manners that they put one at ease, and that directly they said good-bye one would pass completely out of their mind again, they have such a lot of people to see and things to take an interest in.

The King had his little Cairn terrier with him and whilst we were talking two little girls walked across the big yard and curtsied as they went past and the King took off his hat and the terrier rushed across the yard to them. The Queen said "George, do call him back, he might frighten them" and the King said "Oh no, let him alone, he loves to bite bare legs" and roared with laughter.

Then the Queen made me pack up some of my samples of linen and she carried them off to show to her maids in waiting..... On Friday evening on my arrival I dined with Mr Beck, the King's agent, he has a very lovely house overlooking the deer park. This afternoon I am going to tea with Mr and Mrs Cook, the King's gardener, who has a still more beautiful house right in the gardens and surrounded with the most wonderful flower beds you ever saw, but I cannot go till 4.30 as the King and Queen are going to them first, so I expect there will be some nice cakes left over.

If you see any of our relations using table mats instead of table cloths you can tell them that the King hates table mats and told me he would sooner cover his table with a dirty bath towel, if he couldn't afford the laundry expense of table cloths, rather than use table mats....The King has told me to stay here until tomorrow night to give a lecture to his tenants on flax...
Much love, Dad.'

Clearly my father was in quite an exuberant mood when he wrote this letter, which is not surprising. Some of his statements should be taken with a pinch of salt, for example the '2000 acre' promises, as he wasn't averse to some exaggeration on occasion, to heighten the effect. In actual fact the acreages of flax grown by the King and by Mr W. (Billy) Parker in 1933 were 30 and 32 respectively, though these rose to around 50 each in 1934, according to my father's detailed map. All the same, this letter makes it clear that the King and Queen were genuinely interested in the flax-growing project and keen to help it get off to a good start. Future events showed that their interest was not just a flash in the pan.

Chapter 8.   The Flax Factory and Norfolk Flax Ltd.

The King's support and the offer of suitable land on the Royal Estate meant that the next vital step could be taken: construction of a factory which would allow all the necessary processes between growing the flax and spinning its fibres to be done locally, without any need to transport huge quantities of straw across the Irish Sea. First, however, financial backing was needed and here some members of the Irish and Scottish linen trade came to the rescue. They decided to form a limited company, known as Norfolk Flax, with £6,000 capital, to pay for construction of a small flax factory on the Sandringham estate. They were encouraged by the fact that a number of Norfolk farmers had responded positively to the LIRA pamphlet on 'Flax for the Linen Industry' by offering to grow flax once the factory was built. Preparations for this did not go altogether smoothly however. There were delays, which disappointed the King[1]. One possible reason was the abolition of the Empire Marketing Board at about this time. This Board, with the Northern Ireland Government, was responsible for the original 1929

Sowing seed on the royal estate, Paston's Clump, 1933

grant to LIRA for the construction of an experimental flax factory at Lambeg, in which all the components of flax production and processing could be studied. This successful project had allowed all 250 tons of the 1933 Norfolk crop to be processed completely in a series of more or less continuous operations. The Norfolk flax experiment was regarded as a logical successor to the Lambeg scheme, since it was designed to produce an economic factory in miniature, which only needed the replication of its buildings and plant to make it full-scale. Perhaps it was hoped that the Board would help to finance the Norfolk development, until it was chopped. Another snag was opposition to the scheme by an official committee, which seemed to think that LIRA was getting too involved in financial transactions which would encourage flax growing elsewhere than in Northern Ireland[2].

At the end of 1933 there was still uncertainty, but matters must have been settled quite quickly in 1934, as Norfolk Flax Limited came into existence that year and the factory was built in time to deal with the 1934 crop that autumn and winter. Its site by the Babingley river near the Royal village of West Newton was precisely that earmarked by Gilbert Searle as being the most suitable. A large barn was the first to go up, in August 1934, soon to be followed by deseeding and seed-cleaning equipment, retting tanks and the scutching plant. In 1935, the plant breeding research work, which had been carried out at Lambeg ever since 1920, was

The first flax factory at West Newton, erected 1934

44

also transferred to the Sandringham estate at Flitcham Abbey, so called because the house was built round the shell of an Augustinian priory. This became the Searle family home for the next 21 years until the 'Norfolk Flax Experiment' (indeed the *English* Flax Experiment) finally folded. Dr Adelaide G. Davin also moved to Norfolk, making her home in King's Lynn.

Flitcham Abbey, HQ of the 'Norfolk Flax Experiment'

Appropriately, the first recorded visitors to the brand-new Flax Factory were the King and Queen, on February 4th 1935. They watched the deseeding process and the sewing of flax stalks into mats, ready for retting, although neither the retting tanks nor the machinery for scutching the retted straw had been installed yet. Gilbert Searle must have kicked himself for not yet having a Visitors' Book, but their Majesties kindly signed a sheet of Norfolk Flax notepaper which had been sent to Sandringham (see over). This Royal visit received much publicity in *The Times*[3], which also mentioned that Sandringham linen was much used in the Royal Household, e.g. for the King's shirts and the Queen's dresses, perhaps also in future for the sails of the Royal yacht, *Britannia*.

It is interesting to note that all this happened before the land concerned (about 70 acres) 'in the Parish of Flitcham' had been leased to Norfolk Flax Limited. This Lease 'between His Majesty George V by the Grace of God of Great Britain Ireland and the

British Dominions beyond the Seas King Emperor of India' and Norfolk Flax Limited was not signed until May 13th 1935. That was the day on which the 'Royal Sign Manual' was placed on the lease document in the presence of Sir Frederick Ponsonby, Keeper of the Privy Purse and Treasurer to the King. The lease was for a period of 50 years from Jan 1st 1935 at an annual rate of £35 'clear of all deductions', i.e. ten shillings an acre. This would be about £10 an acre in today's money. Everyone seemed happy with it at the time but it caused some trouble after the War when the scale of operations had increased considerably and the value of money had fallen.

This was the King's only visit to England's only flax factory. Less than a year later, on Jan. 20th 1936, his life was 'moving peacefully to its close'. However, his widow, Queen Mary, visited it at least twice more, in 1938 and 1939, shortly before the outbreak of war.

There was one other special event at the Flax Factory in 1935 in which George V played a part, though only indirectly. This was on October 2nd, when Norfolk Flax Limited had an Inspection Day and Luncheon there. This certainly wasn't a low-key affair; in fact its main purpose must have been to publicize this new enterprise as much as possible, both in Britain and Northern Ireland, with the help of reporters from *The Times* and three Belfast newspapers. The importance attached in Northern Ireland to this boost for home flax production is shown by the presence of Viscount Craigavon as one of the guests. He had been Prime Minister of Northern Ireland for over 14 years, having been appointed to this position after passage of the Government of Ireland Act in December 1920 which led to the separation of Ulster from the rest of Ireland (the Irish Free State) and the formation of a Parliament in the North. James Craig had been an Ulster Unionist M.P. in the British Parliament since 1906 after serving in the Boer War and had then become right hand man to the redoubtable Sir Edward Carson, chiefly responsible for keeping Ulster as part of the United Kingdom and separate from Irish Home Rule. The early years of his premiership had been very difficult, with widespread violence because of partition. Gradually some sort of order was established although 'the Troubles' lingered on, as A.G.S. remembers from his boyhood in Belfast.

Other guests included two more M.P.s, representatives from Government Ministries, members of learned societies and associations connected with scientific research and with flax processing, Directors and Shareholders of Norfolk Flax Ltd and a number of local farmers, including the King's Agent, Mr A.C.Beck. However, pride of place in the list of local farmers was given to the Dowager Viscountess, Dorothy Downe. She lived in Hillington Hall, about half way between Flitcham Abbey and the Flax Factory, and had already grown 10 acres of flax in 1933. She was clearly one of the landed gentry, but few locals can have realised how extreme were her political views. She was in fact an active member of Sir Oswald Mosley's British Union of Fascists, as Daniel Farson makes clear in his fascinating biography of the very gifted writer, Henry Williamson, author of 'Tarka the Otter', 'The Flax of Dream', 'The Story of a Norfolk Farm' and much else[4]. Apparently, it was Lady Downe who persuaded Williamson, an admirer of 'the great man across the Rhine'[5] to join the B.U.F. in 1937, the year he bought a Norfolk farm in Stiffkey. Subsequently he met Mosley when 'The Leader' was staying with Lady Downe at Hillington Hall[6].

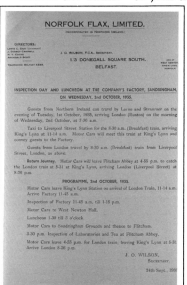

By the time of the Inspection Gilbert Searle had moved to Flitcham Abbey and had supervised construction of the Flax Factory, so was responsible for all the local preparations. Inevitably, he was bombarded with letters from Mr J. O. Wilson, the Secretary of Norfolk Flax in Belfast. First there was the problem of who would meet the N.I. Prime Minister and others at King's Lynn railway station and who at the Flax Factory. The Chairman of Norfolk Flax, Lewis Gray, decided to welcome Lord Craigavon at the Factory, while a Director, Archibald Scott, would take him there in 'one of the Daimler cars'. Major Searle would be needed at the station to shepherd lesser mortals into the buses, but would also be

47

needed at the Factory. So 'unless you have lost your nerve, I think you could be the last to leave King's Lynn and yet the first to arrive at the Factory.' This rather suggests that he was a reckless driver, but he wasn't! Then someone had suggested that Union Jacks should be flown but Searle pooh-poohed the idea:- 'You are quite right about the Union Jacks,' wrote Wilson, 'living on this side one has to advertise the fact that they are loyal. It is not necessary on your side.' Then there was the all-important question of the menu for luncheon, to be held in West Newton Hall on the Royal Estate. The quotation of 4 shillings a head was accepted as very reasonable (if not incredible) but Mr Scott thought there should be a second fish ('he thinks fried sole') and chicken as well as beef and mutton, because 'a great many people nowadays suffer from blood pressure and are not allowed either beef or mutton.' Then 'at all costs the table cloths and table napkins must be ALL LINEN and of fairly good quality.'

All went according to plan: first the factory inspection and then the sumptuous lunch. In the end, this cost 4 shillings and sixpence a head for the 58 people who attended, exclusive of drinks (which included Irish and Scotch whisky, sherry and port) and quite a few cigars. The party then set off for Flitcham Abbey, which was only a couple of miles away, to inspect the new laboratories and have tea, before returning to King's Lynn to catch the London train or to Peterborough for Lord Craigavon to catch the train to Heysham and boat back to Belfast. The total cost of the 'Show', as Searle called it, was only £31, which even included the hire of cars and coaches. The weather was excellent and the importance of this event was brought into focus by a telegram from the King to Lord Craigavon:- 'I am so glad to hear that you have been able to find time to see the flax grown in Norfolk. Shall be interested to know what you think of the crops as I am, of course, anxious that the growing of flax in Norfolk should be a success. George R.I.'[7] It was indeed a success, but sadly the King would not live to see his efforts come to fruition.

Dear Mr Wilson,

I might telegraphed you the cost of the Show, as I thought you might want it for a Board Meeting. I am not sending yo[u] the actual accounts, as I suppose you do not want to see them until they are paid. The details are as follows :-

Motor Coach			£2	10	0
75 menu cards				12	6
Luncheon	58 at 4/6	£13-1-0			
	Irish	14-0			
	Scotch	14-0			
	Sherry	1-14-0			
	Port	1 -1-0			
	Other drinks	1-16-10			
	Cigars 17	10-6			
	Cigarettes	2-9			
	Matches	7	19	14	8
Cars, Oct 1&2 Peterborough	5-10-6		5	10	0
Flitcham tea our expenses were			2	12	0
Hire of West Newton Hall				5	0
			£31	4	2

48

Chapter 9. Enter and exit Edward VIII (AGS)

Less than four months later King George V was dead and a drastically different Royal régime was in operation. Balmoral and Sandringham became the private property of King Edward VIII, who disliked both of them, as they were associated with 'some of the most boring and unhappy periods of his life'[1]. In *A King's Story* the Duke of Windsor describes Sandringham as a 'voracious white elephant', which apparently cost £50,000 a year to run[2]. He must have been tempted to sell it, lock, stock and barrel, but decided first to see what economies could be made. For this purpose he persuaded his brother Bertie (then Duke of York, later King George VI), to go down there with the Earl of Radnor (an agricultural expert who later became Chairman of the Forestry Commission) and discover ways of running it more cheaply. They visited the Flax Factory on Feb. 19th 1936, only four weeks into the new reign, which shows how eager the King was to make some savings. I doubt whether the Royal Duke and the Earl found any opportunities for these at the Flax Factory: its very low rent was fixed for 50 years and was part of a leasehold agreement which was less than one year old. However, as a result of their enquiries at Sandringham it was recommended to the new King's Agent, Captain W. A. Fellowes, that a quarter of the 400 Royal staff there should be made redundant[1]. What the King was trying to do on the Estate became common knowledge and did not add to his popularity. I well remember as a schoolboy hearing dark mutterings to the effect that 'what we need is another Royal funeral.'

King Edward visited Sandringham only once during his reign, but saw both the Flax Factory and Flitcham Abbey on that occasion (October 19th to 22nd 1936). Perhaps it is not surprising that this visit took place just at the time when his beloved Wallis Simpson (later the Duchess of Windsor) had to seclude herself in Felixstowe while waiting for her divorce petition to be heard in Ipswich. The Royal appearance at Flitcham Abbey had nothing to do with the flax research in the new laboratories there, but a lot to do with

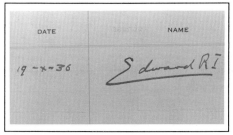

DATE	NAME
19 -x-36	*Edward R I*

shooting pheasants and partridges in the area, since the King used the place as a lunch-stop for the only Royal shooting-party of his reign. My sister (Mrs B. M. Matthews) tells me that there were only about a couple of days' notice of the impending visitation. Then up rolled an enormous shooting-brake, full of crockery, cutlery, food, drink and flunkeys, who took over the place. The food was served in our fairly large dining-room, with pictures of tippling monks on the wall. Afterwards, my sister found an unsmoked cigarette on the mantelpiece and kept it as a memento.

The King seems to have spent much of his time at the Abbey pacing up and down the lawn in front of the house. He must indeed have had a great deal on his mind during that particular week in October, when the crisis which arose because of his determination to marry Mrs Simpson was just looming on the horizon. On Sunday, October 18th, the King had driven off from Fort Belvedere, near Windsor, ostensibly bound for Sandringham. However, instead of going straight there, it seems that he went to Felixstowe[3] to meet Mrs Simpson secretly. He then resumed his journey to Sandringham, which he reached at 4 a.m. the following day. He was then told that his Private Secretary (Major Alexander Hardinge) wished to speak to him urgently. The King 'phoned him at 9 a.m. and heard that the Prime Minister, Stanley Baldwin, had asked for an audience to discuss the impending Simpson divorce proceedings. He agreed to meet Baldwin at 10 a.m. next day (Oct 20th) but at Fort Belvedere rather than Sandringham, to ensure complete privacy[4]. In the meantime, he must have spent a busy day at Sandringham, since it was then that he visited the Flax Factory and toured the farms on his Estate, giving 'bonuses to workmen'[5].

On Tuesday October 20th, while his shooting party gathered at Sandringham, the King met Baldwin in the garden at Fort Belvedere. The Prime Minister tried to persuade him to have the divorce proceedings postponed but met with no success. The King insisted that this was Mrs Simpson's private business, with which he had no right to interfere. 'You and I must settle this matter together,' he told the PM 'I will not have anyone interfering.' This was the first of eight meetings between the two, before the crisis was finally settled by the King's abdication on December 10th. The general public knew of the constitutional crisis only about a week before it was finally settled although the American papers had been shouting about it for months! This could hardly happen nowadays.

The King returned to Sandringham that evening to greet his shooting-party guests, who included the Earl of Harewood, Sir Samuel Hoare, Sir Humphrey de Trafford and Mr Harry Brown, a racehorse trainer. At that time, Sir Samuel Hoare (later Viscount Templewood) was First Lord of the Admiralty in Baldwin's Government, after occupying other important positions, including Foreign Secretary. However, he had to resign from the Foreign Office in 1935 because of the outcry over the 'Hoare-Laval plan' which proposed giving Italy (which had invaded Abyssinia under Mussolini's dictatorship) a large chunk of Abyssinian territory. It is worth pointing out, however, that he was also four times Secretary of State for Air and did much to encourage air communications within the Commonwealth. He was known to be an excellent shot and when he tendered his resignation to George V the King told him to 'go and shoot a lot of woodcock in Norfolk'![6] The Earl of Harewood was the King's brother-in-law, having married the Princess Royal, and was also his personal ADC. Both he and Sir Humphrey de Trafford were educated at Eton and Sandhurst and had served with distinction in the Great War; no doubt they were also good shots. The background of Mr Brown remains a mystery.

It is recorded[7] that on Thursday Oct. 22nd, when the party went shooting over the coverts at Anmer, the King took a photograph of the group and then handed his camera to a guest, to include himself in it. This record of his only shooting-party has survived[3]. That evening the King and his guests left Sandringham, the King going to Buckingham Palace to receive a visitor, the Crown Prince of Denmark. He was at a Privy Council meeting there on the 27th when news came through that Mrs Simpson had been granted a decree nisi because of her husband's alleged adultery in Bray with a lady called Buttercup Kennedy[4]. The King celebrated with Wallis, but the crisis deepened.

The King's choice of Anmer and Flitcham for the shooting drives may have been connected with his decision to sell these two parts of his estate, which might make this a last opportunity to

51

shoot over them. A contract was drawn up and only awaited final signature, but then came December 10th and the Abdication. Eight days later the new King (George VI) could tell his mother, Queen Mary: 'I have stopped the sale of Anmer', no doubt of Flitcham also[1]. This may have saved the Norfolk Flax Experiment, as both the Flax Factory and the research laboratories were in the parish of Flitcham-with-Anmer, so presumably involved in the proposed sale. A buyer might have had radically different ideas on how to use the land. Perhaps he was the mysterious Mr Harry Brown, possibly invited to join the shooting party so that he could survey his prospective estate. In view of subsequent events it seems worth recording one particular visitor to the Flax Factory during the reign of Edward VIII, namely Mr B. Page of the Admiralty, on July 29th 1936. He became a frequent war-time visitor and, with his wife, a personal friend of my father and stepmother.

Stanley Baldwin clutching a bale of scutched Sandringham flax, with Dr W.H.Gibson, second Director of LIRA.

Chapter 10. Crisis as war-clouds gather

George VI came to the throne at a very difficult time for Great Britain and its allies. The aggressive intentions of the German and Italian dictatorships became clear to all except some political ostriches. Futile attempts at appeasement ensured that Mussolini conquered all of Abyssinia and then joined with Hitler to form the 'Rome-Berlin Axis'. Hitler had denounced the Treaty of Versailles and introduced conscription; German troops then marched into the demilitarised Rhineland. Hitler then denounced the 1925 Treaty of Locarno, by which Britain, France and Germany agreed permanently to accept established frontiers in Western Europe. The League of Nations (from which Germany had withdrawn) was too weak and ineffective to do more than protest when solemn agreements were flouted. Soon (1938) Hitler would annex Austria and then turn the heat on Czechoslovakia.

In the first year of the King's reign (1937) flax-growing and processing on the Royal Estate continued much as before, with a total acreage of about 250 being devoted to the crop. In 1938, however, a labour-saving change in the way the flax plants were processed was tried out with great success, namely the elimination of the laborious and expensive retting process. This followed the 1934 invention by LIRA scientists at Lambeg of the LINRA crimper breaker. This allowed unretted straw to be scutched, with production of a fibre which was very suitable for dry spinning without further treatment. The resultant fabric was not fine enough to make into damask tablecloths or other household linens but was ideal for the production of naval canvases, hose-pipes and other strong and durable items needed by the Navy and other Services. Much of the Norfolk flax straw was processed in this way, then spun and woven in Scotland to give some 20,000 yards of cloth of the type specified by the Admiralty, which gave very satisfactory results on testing. The Admiralty came to realise that this Norfolk flax straw would be an ideal substitute for the Baltic flaxes used in the past, which in war-time would be difficult or impossible to obtain. Decisive action was imperative in view of the worsening international situation so, at the end of 1938, they reserved for their own use the whole stock of straw and pedigree seed stored at the West Newton Flax Factory.

In 1938 the Czech crisis over the Sudeten German borderlands came to a head and war seemed inevitable, since France was pledged to support Czechoslovakia. With Mussolini's cunning help, however, the Prime Minister (Neville Chamberlain) managed to engineer the Munich Agreement, in which the dictator was appeased once again by being given the Sudetenlands forthwith, without consulting the Czechs at all. Chamberlain came home waving a piece of paper and declaring that it was 'peace in our time'! He was proved wrong only too soon. The Nazis marched into Prague early in 1939 and dismembered the rest of Czechoslovakia. Clearly Hitler would stop at nothing, so it became essential to prepare for war. This meant, among a multitude of other measures, planning for a vast increase in home flax production.

In late 1938, however, a crisis blew up which threatened the very existence of the Norfolk flax experiment and all it entailed. The Northern Ireland Government gave a grant of £150,000 to its linen industry to encourage more flax to be grown in the Province. None of this money was available for the Norfolk enterprise, even though all of the work there was designed to help the Ulster linen industry, by providing it with more raw material of high quality. It seemed as though Irish financial support for the Norfolk flax experiment was coming to an end just when a rapid expansion of the effort there was urgently needed, both with respect to the acreage grown and the experimental work on green scutching to satisfy naval needs.

To avert this crisis, it was absolutely vital that an alternative source of funds be located without delay. The rescue package was organized just in time by a 'public-spirited Scottish manufacturer', as Gilbert Searle later called him in a memo to the King, who promised to provide the necessary financial help to allow the Flax Factory to maintain full production and to move forwards towards a war footing. This anonymous and modest benefactor was in fact Mr R. Wemyss Honeyman, whose Scottish firm (D. S. Honeyman Ltd.) was one of the shareholders of Norfolk Flax.

Chapter 11. The King is briefed, the Admiralty takes over (AGS)

This temporary funding by Honeyman saved Norfolk Flax from extinction, but something more permanent was needed to ensure that it contributed fully to the war effort. Here the King himself seems to have played a significant role. Obviously he was in a strong position to express his views; both flax factory and research laboratories were on his land, so he was naturally interested in what happened to them. Moreover, he was very well briefed on all aspects of the crisis, thanks to a 3-page document on 'The Norfolk Flax Experiment'[1] which my father drafted and gave to him personally on December 29th, 1938, at Flitcham Abbey.

He came to our home on a foggy day in the Christmas holidays. There was a feeling of hushed excitement in the air and we boys knew we had to keep quiet and well out of sight. Captain (later Sir William) Fellowes, the King's Agent, drove him on the short journey from Sandringham to Flitcham Abbey. In a letter to my father from the Sandringham Estate Office, written nearly twenty years later, he recalled that memorable occasion: 'It seems a long time ago when I motored the King to see you at Flitcham in the fog.'

Captain Fellowes (left) inspects Flitcham housing plans with Queen Mary and Council officers

All we heard were murmurs as my father greeted his visitors and ushered them into his office-cum-study, which was separated from the dining-room by the eight-foot thickness of a monastery wall. He must then have presented the King with his memo on the flax production crisis and proceeded to go through it item by item. He would have pointed out that the Norfolk flax operations were based entirely on the Royal estate and financed by Norfolk Flax Ltd., founded by LIRA because they were not allowed to trade for profit but wanted to extend flax research to a semi-commercial scale, as well as continuing with their successful plant-breeding work. The plant and equipment at the Factory, which received no Government support, would have to be greatly increased if large-scale operations became necessary. The Services were large consumers of linen goods; it was reckoned that in war-time they would need the products of about 100,000 acres of flax, about 30,000 acres for the Admiralty alone. Since both the Irish and the Scottish linen industries depended very heavily on flax from Belgium, Holland and the Baltic countries, which could well be cut off by Germany in time of war, it was of great importance to increase home flax production as soon as possible. Instead, Norfolk Flax Ltd was threatened with closure. Because of this threat, and because trials of unretted Norfolk flax straw (to produce strong and durable cloth of the type needed by the Admiralty) had yielded such promising results, the Admiralty had reserved the whole stock of straw and pedigree seed in Norfolk for their own purposes. However, further research work was needed on the mechanics of processing unretted straw to give the sort of end-product required by the Services.

My father concluded that Norfolk Flax should become a 'full scale Government Research Station' and should be prepared for rapid expansion, first to a properly equipped nucleus dealing with 2,000 acres. However, the Admiralty didn't feel able to finance the experimental work, neither apparently did the Board of Trade nor the Ministry of Agriculture. In fact, the situation looked bleak that Christmas-time. Clearly, the powers that be had not woken up to the urgency of the situation, not knowing that war with the Axis powers was less than nine months away and that the Low Countries would be overrun less than nine months later. Russian flax exports were suspended even before the war started.

We may never know what positive steps King George VI took to ensure the continuation of the Norfolk flax enterprise, but we can be fairly sure he did his best. My father evidently thought so since, in a letter to Captain Fellowes many years later (1957) he wrote: 'It was the late King's powerful advocacy which led very fortunately to a wartime flax industry being set up.' Moreover, only three weeks after that meeting at Flitcham there was another one at the Board of Trade in London to discuss 'the future of the Norfolk Flax Experimental Station.' As a result of that meeting it was decided the following July that the Norfolk Experimental Station should be taken over by the Government in its entirety, staff included, and should be under the control of the Admiralty until a Ministry of Supply was set up in 1940. What a relief that must have been to all concerned and what a flurry of feverish activity it must have generated!

First, arrangements had to be made for the transfer of Major Searle, Miss Davin and other 'salaried officers' from LIRA employment to Government employment with H.M. Norfolk Flax Establishment, as the new entity was called, with my father now called the 'Superintendent'. Second, all the buildings and equipment belonging to Norfolk Flax Ltd had to be acquired by the Admiralty and the Honeyman loan repaid. This loan by Messrs D. S. Honeyman, of Kirkcaldy, Scotland, to Norfolk Flax had allowed considerable extensions to the Factory buildings to be started and much new equipment to be acquired before the outbreak of war and at a time of great uncertainty. Thus in 1939 a crop of 1,000 acres of flax could be grown and processed, indeed a very wise move. Transfer of the holdings of Norfolk Flax Ltd to the Admiralty was done by acquiring all the issued capital of the Company in the form of shares, appointing new shareholders and directors, then winding up the Company and transferring its assets to the Admiralty. Lease of the Flax Factory land from the King also had to be transferred to the Admiralty.

On October 1st 1939, shortly after the outbreak of war with Germany, H.M. Norfolk Flax Establishment came into being as a Government concern, with Fleet Order 3884/39 outlining the operational arrangements. It had its own Imprest account and was treated rather as if it was a new destroyer being fitted out. On the same day the three salaried staff, namely Major G. O. Searle, Dr

Adelaide G. Davin and Mr R. McCotter, were transferred from LIRA to the Admiralty. Soon, an Agricultural Officer (Mr R. L. Freeman-Taylor) and a full-time Factory Manager (Mr V. Halstead) were to join them. The whole concern was limbering up for a big expansion of effort.

Chapter 12. Full steam ahead as the battle begins

For flax production at least, what a contrast there was between the 1939 situation and that during World War I, when the flax crisis struck in 1917! With a flax industry already established in Britain this time and with good stocks of pedigree seed it was possible to get off to a flying start. This was especially so because LIRA research had shown that the cumbersome retting process could be omitted when producing the sorts of fabric needed by the Services. The laborious process of flax-pulling had been mechanised, which also saved manpower and time. Only too soon in 1940, after the 'phoney war' period had been followed by German invasion of France and the Low countries, continental sources of flax fibre were denied to us, so it was vital this time that we produced our own.

Flax-pulling by machine
Eastern Daily Press

The first essential was to grow as large an acreage of flax in 1940 as seed stocks would allow. Some other flax enterprises had sprung up in Britain during the previous five years: in Northamptonshire, Kent, Dorset, Derbyshire and Perthshire in Scotland. By far the largest of these was that of Messrs Willett and Bartram at Billing, near Northampton and luckily its crops had been sown

Gaited straw drying in the field

entirely with pedigree Liral seed. The Admiralty bought all their available seed at £2: 17: 6 a hundredweight and distributed it to approved UK growers for the 1940 season, as well as sending a ton to the Ministry of Agriculture, Northern Ireland for it to distribute in that Province. Surprisingly, 5 cwt was also sent to a firm in Holland, B. C. Algra, whose head had already been over to see the Flax Factory - apparently the only pre-war Dutch visitor. The New Zealand Government and its Department of Scientific and Industrial Research showed great interest in the Norfolk flax enterprise, sending several representatives over to inspect the factory at this time. They were sent 2 cwt. of pedigree flax seed to help them contribute to the war effort.

Over 1,000 acres were grown in and around the Royal estate in 1940. Many more centres now started to cultivate flax, as the result of a Government decision to build up the flax industry in Great Britain under the Ministry of Supply. During 1940-41 no less than twelve new mills were built and equipped, while five existing ones were greatly extended[1]. Thirteen of these were in England, one in Wales and three in Scotland. Fifteen were also started in Northern Ireland by private enterprise, although most were smaller than the English mills. All of the British mills were fully equipped with up-to-date deseeding and seed-cleaning plant as well as scutching turbines. This was possible because of the astute and timely purchase of the latest types of these machines from Belgium

The Flax Factory in war-time

in 1939. This could only be done because of the generous loan from Mr R.W.Honeyman, mentioned earlier, which saved Norfolk Flax and allowed vital equipment to be bought in the nick of time. In addition, three Dutch barns were built at the West Newton Flax Factory, in order to house more than 2,000 tons of flax in various stages, ready to be handed over to the Government for war use after further processing. To speed things up a separate de-seeding unit was set up at Drayton, near Norwich[2].

The speed with which the British flax industry expanded to meet the challenge of all-out war is shown by the fact that about 15,000 acres in England and Scotland could be sown with pedigree seed in 1940. This yielded about 60,000 cwt. of pedigree flax seed in time for the spring sowing of 1941. Some non-pedigree seed was also sown at that time, but after 1941 all flax-growers in the British Isles were supplied with pedigree seed, most of which came originally from the pioneer plant-breeding research carried out by the Davin/Searle team in Northern Ireland (LIRA) and then in Norfolk. In addition, the Northern Ireland Ministry of Agriculture, produced and propagated an equally good variety, known as Stormont Gossamer[3]. Seed from the Liral pedigree flax strains (Prince, Monarch, and Crown) and from the Stormont one became of world-wide repute, being distributed not only to the whole of Ireland (whose acreage grew to a war-time peak of 150,000) and Great Britain but also to Australia and New Zealand, Canada,

Kenya and even Egypt, where flax-growing really began. Well over a million acres a year were grown at that time in the Empire as a whole and more than a tenth of the seed for this came directly from the efforts of Norfolk growers. These four pedigree strains increased fibre yield by 50% per acre over that of commercial strains.

Flax supplies from the near Continent were cut off in mid-1940 by the German invasion of France and the Low Countries. However, Great Britain's potential for flax fibre production at that critical time was vastly better than in 1917, the equivalent time of crisis in the first World War. A flax industry had already been planned, provision of buildings and equipment was well advanced and seed supply was secure. Moreover, two important advances in methods of processing the flax had been made. First, pulling the flax in the fields could now be done by machine rather than by hand, unless the crop had been flattened by bad weather. The first really practical pulling machine was one of Messrs. Boby, made in Suffolk and first used in Norfolk in 1933. The enormous expansion of flax-growing in Britain at the start of the war forced a similar

Flax-pulling machines awaiting delivery to growers

surge in flax-puller improvement and production since the skilled labour for hand-pulling just was not available. 'In the early years,' wrote Major Searle in 1946,[3] 'some of the teething troubles nearly sent us crazy', but thanks to the 'magnificent efforts' of Messrs Boby the required number of machines, capable of harvesting 8-10 acres a day in an undamaged state, did materialise. A fleet of forty of these 'Boby Pullers' were used in Norfolk alone, with more money spent on them than on any other item in the flax-production budget.[2]

The second advance came with the discovery (already mentioned) that the tedious process of retting the straw could be omitted when products were for service use (canvases, hose-pipes, aeroplane fabrics etc.) rather than the fine linens of domestic use (sheets, tablecloths etc.). A special machine was designed at the LIRA Institute, Lambeg, to carry out this 'green-scutching'. This fairly drastic change in technique also led to some problems, especially in Scotland, and in 1943 the Parliamentary Select

Stacking pulled flax

Committee on National Expenditure recommended that 'retting should be re-introduced wherever possible to increase the yield and the quality of the fibre'[4]. However, the Ministry of Supply disputed this recommendation. It pointed out that half the flax output was required for a particular war purpose, while most of the rest was used in the manufacture of wartime canvases. Green (unretted) flax gave fibre of the right quality for these purposes[5]. So its production was continued.

The House of Commons Select Committee on National Expenditure had the important job of looking at all aspects of the British war effort, to make sure that money was not being wasted. The small group of M.P.s making up the committee included such well-known figures as Dame Irene Ward and Mr Alfred Bossom. They visited the Flax Factory in early January 1943 and may not have been terribly happy with everything they saw. This can be surmised from one of the recommendations in their report:- 'That all flax factories should be examined by Government inspectors *in view of unhealthy conditions which undoubtedly exist'*. The need to improve dust-extraction was emphasised; reminiscences of those who worked at the West Newton factory during the war show just how frightful the dust problem was. The Committee also complained that the cost of production in the flax industry was about twice the notional value of the product, but this is hardly surprising given the speed and urgency with which the industry had to be expanded to meet wartime needs and the initially bad seasons which made harvesting very difficult. One wonders, too, how the 'notional value' of a crop is determined when it is essential for the war effort.

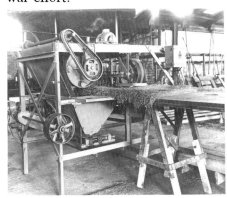

LIRA deseeding machine

Of the two M.P.s mentioned above, Irene Ward was probably the more distinguished.[7] Later in her long Parliamentary career she became a Dame, a Companion of Honour and a Baroness (of North Tyneside). She was a most energetic M.P. who campaigned fiercely for constituency and other interests, which included fisheries, shipbuilding, nurses and midwives. She was famous for her back-bench heckling, was responsible for four Acts of Parliament and eventually became the longest-serving member of the House. Besides the Select Committee on Expenditure, she also served during the War years on a Ministry of Labour committee which dealt with the national call-up of women. She died in 1980. Alfred Bossom, who also ended up in the House of Lords (as a Baron), was an architect by training who built up a considerable international practice[8]. He was already 50 when elected M.P. for Maidstone but held on to that Conservative stronghold for the next 28 years. During that time he became Chairman or President of a remarkable number of Anglo-foreign Unions, e.g. Belgium, Brazil, Luxemburg, Texas, and was awarded

64

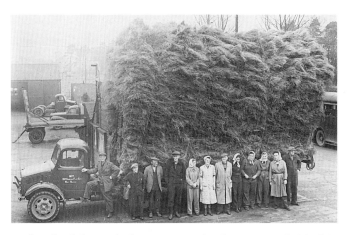

**A lorry-load of deseeded straw on the factory weighbridge with
driver Joe Pinder and other HMNFE employees**

an impressive number of foreign honours as a result. The attach-
ment of His Majesty's Norfolk Flax Establishment to the Admiralty
was only a temporary measure until the Government set up a
Ministry of Supply. The Establishment was transferred to this in
October 1940 and became the research centre for the Home Flax
Production Scheme, being chiefly responsible for the supply of
pedigree flax seed. The Ministry set up a Directorate of Home Flax
Production to co-ordinate the country-wide growing and processing
of flax, encouraging more farmers to grow it and advising them on
how to do so successfully and as efficiently as possible, through a
series of informative leaflets.

**Bales of
scutched flax**

65

Chapter 13. Earl De La Warr rallies the flax teams

For most of its war-time existence the Flax Directorate was led by a remarkable aristocrat: Herbrand Edward Dundonald Brassey Sackville, 9th Earl De La Warr, but known universally as 'Buck'[1]. He was educated at Eton (where he founded the Eton College Political Society) and Magdalen College Oxford. He succeeded to the Earldom at the early age of 15, during the Great War, and subsequently joined the Trawler section of the Royal Naval Reserve as an able seaman, since he had a conscientious objection to killing people at that time. Nevertheless, he became Parliamentary Under-Secretary to the War Office in 1929 and rose rapidly through a series of such posts to join the Cabinet of Neville Chamberlain as Lord Privy Seal in 1937. It was at this stage that his career faltered, apparently because he declared that he would face war to free the world from the constant threat of ultimata. This did not tally with Chamberlain's policy of appeasement and De La Warr was demoted to the post of President of the Board of Education. He was not invited to join Churchill's War Cabinet; instead, he became Chairman of the Ministry of Supply's Flax Control Board in 1941 and then succeeded Mr N. Isaacs as Director of Home Flax Production in July 1943. For this post he accepted no salary.

The job was no sinecure and he threw himself into it with great enthusiasm, dedication and skill. It was absolutely vital for the war effort that flax production in this country was rapidly increased, when all the usual sources of foreign supply were closed to us and despite the natural reluctance of farmers to grow this unfamiliar crop. Moreover, weather conditions in 1940 and 1941 were appalling, with much of the flax straw not fit to be processed, so a lot of persuasion was needed. However, Earl De La Warr did the trick by constantly touring the whole of the United Kingdom (including Northern Ireland) to address large groups of farmers, visit the flax factories and generally help people to realise that growing and processing flax really was a most essential part of the war effort. The fact that he grew flax himself must have helped

Earl De La Warr (left), with G. O. Searle beside him, examining a flax sample

considerably in getting his message across. For instance, he pointed out in 1943 that at the start of the war the country was growing 400 acres of flax for fibre, in three years this had been increased to 50,000 acres and they were aiming even higher. He added that 'The pullers were 60% better last year than they were the year before and they would be still better this year. Last year they turned out just three and a half times more fibre from the factories than the year before. It was two grades higher in quality than the previous year and the cost was also down considerably.'[2] In Belfast he told reporters: 'Ulster is Britain's No. 1 area for flax supplies and we are anxious to see the acreage increased to 100,000 next year (1943).'[3] In Somerset he wondered: 'going round the country, whether farmers growing flax and workers handling it in the factories realise that this is one of the great production adventures of the war'. He added that production was such that they had been able to satisfy every service order with which they had been presented. The bulk of the production was going into parachute harness; and every pound of flax grown that had gone through the factories had gone for essential war service[4]. In Yorkshire, he said: 'The need of flax for war purposes is going to be greater next year than it has ever been... Supplies are coming in from Ireland, New Zealand, Egypt and a little from Kenya. Meanwhile the demand is increasing for flax for parachute harness, and it's not just a question of parachutes for the Air Force but for more intensive purposes. The rate of aeroplane production must increase, and flax is needed to cover wings, make ropes, naval canvas and in the construction of Service boots and also agricultural labourers' boots. Now a great order has come from the Navy for flax for the construction of apparatus used in amphibious operations. We are asking you here in Yorkshire to give us 3,000 instead of 2,500 acres...'[5]

Lord De La Warr continued in his key position in the British flax industry until well after the end of the war, only resigning in July 1949. However, from 1944-1949 he also served as Chairman of the Agricultural Research Council, for agriculture was his overriding interest. He then resumed his political career with his appointment as Postmaster-General by Winston Churchill in 1951, a post which he held on to until Churchill had to retire in 1955. He was largely responsible for several important developments in telecommunication during his time in office, e.g. international telex, letter-sorting machines, planning national telephone numbers and the introduction of commercial television, the last encountering very strenuous opposition in the Lords. He remained an active member of that august 'club' for the rest of his life, which ended on the pavement outside St James's Palace as he walked to the theatre.

The boost to flax-growing given by the mass meetings of farmers country-wide at which Earl De La Warr and others spoke was supplemented in 1943 by a mobile exhibition called 'Flax goes to War' which toured actual and potential flax-growing areas to publicize its many wartime uses[6]. These included linen for covering parts of Wellesley and Wellington bombers as well as Hurricane fighters in the Middle East and Fleet Air Arm Gladiator fighters and Swordfish torpedo-bombers. Flax fibre was also vitally important for parachute lines and harness, of which vast quantities were needed when airborne operations, involving thousands of paratroops, were mounted. It was also essential for ARP (air raid precautions) fire-hose for both its lightness and strength, since nothing else could withstand the great water pressures. It was also needed for webbing, for many types of naval canvas and as a backing to the steel body armour designed for airmen. Because of its toughness and strength, linen thread was used to stitch soldiers', miners' and farm workers' boots. It also made very durable fishing nets, especially for salmon.

The impressive war-time increase in the acreage under flax in England and Wales was also emphasised in this exhibition: from a mere 400 in 1939 to 52,000 in 1943, as well as 50,000 in Scotland and about 100,000 in Northern Ireland. At the same time, the acreage needed to produce one ton of scutched fibre fell from 17 acres in 1941 to about 6.5 in 1943.

In 1943, Gilbert Searle was awarded the OBE (Officer of the Order of the British Empire) for his services to the war effort, by helping to re-start the flax industry in Britain before the war, keeping it alive, preparing it for the onslaught and helping to build it up to full production.

Chapter 14. War-time work and play on the Royal Estate

The original Flax Factory on the Royal Estate at West Newton was just as busy in war-time as all its more recent companions. No less than 5,662 acres of flax were grown around Sandringham in 1944, for instance. In order to process all this a 24-hour work plan was needed during the 5-day week, with three 8-hour shifts. Conditions were far from ideal, as the reminiscences of those who worked there over 50 years ago show only too clearly. Much of the work was in the scutching-room where there was a terrible amount of dust, even after extractor fans were fitted. Sometimes in summer the heat was 'diabolical'. Conditions were so bad once that the workers tried to

Workers in the scutching shed with Ted Kay, manager
Left to Right: Miss E. Wilson, Mr J. Duprey, Mr E. T. Kay, Miss A. Wittred, Miss P. Athow

go on strike, but this was essential national service, to which one was directed, so they probably just had to 'grin and bear it'. Other jobs included baling and tidying up dried, retted straw before it was sent to be scutched, but most of it was green-scutched without being retted. In summer, workers were sent flax-pulling sometimes, but certain fields were full of frogs, which terrified some of the girls! Pulling machines were also used but their belts kept coming off, especially if they encountered the tough weed known as 'fat hen' - a member of the goosefoot family.

Women hand-pulling flax
Lynn News & Advertiser

Fortunately, the factory itself was never bombed, but two of its young female workers were injured when the Eagle pub was bombed in King's Lynn in 1942. They were visited in hospital by the Duke of Kent, who lost his life on active service later the same year (Aug. 25th). The Flax Factory itself was visited by Queen Mary in August 1939, just before the war began, by Princess Marina, Duchess of Kent, in August 1941 and by King George VI and Queen Elizabeth, with their daughters Elizabeth (our present Queen) and Margaret in January 1945 (see over). There seems to have been a mammoth cleaning-up operation before this last visit.

The Royal family saving petrol at Sandringham in 1943
Hulton Getty Collection

71

Of course there was a lighter side to work at the factory. Apparently, some fun and games were associated with the bales of flax straw, since one former worker remembers a brand-new set of false teeth being lost on top of one. Vivian from Roydon told fortunes in the Canteen, where ENSA concerts were sometimes held at lunch-time, when comedians, pianists, singers and 'Workers' Playtime' helped to keep up morale. There were even dances at the Drayton deseeding station. No one complained of the canteen food, which was described as 'good' or 'reasonable', with 'plenty of potatoes and gravy'. Clearly there was an efficient Manageress who stood no nonsense. Perhaps the only exception was when the workers somehow managed to upset a cook on the night-shift, who then (it is alleged) put something in the mince which gave them all diarrhoea.

The drivers interviewed (by J.W.T.) told stories of their many adventures and of each other's reputations. One was well-known for speeding and was stopped twice by police for driving at more than 24 mph! Another was constantly losing his load through cornering too fast. Another one had to stop at a level-crossing, whereupon an errant spark from the passing engine set his highly inflammable straw load alight. Another (lady) driver had to chase a train which her passenger (who was 'always late') had missed but also ran into trouble at a level-crossing, where she crashed the car in her haste and later was left to fend for herself by her ungallant passenger. Often the drivers had to work long hours and travel great distances to deliver loads to far-away factories, pick up broken-down cars after repair and so on. One of the well-remembered and rather troublesome cars was the boss's grey Riley (BAH 391), with a pre-selector gear-box which used to freeze each winter.

Flitcham Abbey was the Research Headquarters for the British flax industry during and after the war, but there were research and office staff at the West Newton factory too. At its peak, the scientific staff at the two centres, comprising scientists, scientific officers, experimental officers, laboratory assistants and laboratory attendants (the usual Scientific Civil Service hierarchy) totalled 40, with Dr

The flax laboratories at the rear of Flitcham Abbey

Adelaide G. Davin as overall Head of Research. There were also about twelve Office Staff, who had to deal with all the documents, as well as much filing and typing work. Contracts had to be sent out to all the local farmers growing flax, of which there were 500 at the time of peak production, as well as a series of crop reports for each flax field on its state from sowing to harvesting. It is no wonder that the staff had to work long hours: from 9 a.m. to 6 p.m. Monday to Friday and 9 a.m. to 1 p.m. on Saturday. They had fewer opportunities for entertainment than the factory workers, but there were play-readings in which both office and scientific staff took part, as well as the occasional concert in the Village Hall at Hillington, which is about half way between Flitcham and West Newton. One of the performances there was of 'Maria Marten', a play in which there is a hanging scene. Unfortunately the actor concerned - John Cullen, a scientific officer at Flitcham Abbey - slipped when faking the hanging scene and would have hung himself in reality if he had not been rescued by David Gilling. 'Sonny' Knight, the gardener at Flitcham Abbey, was a star turn at the concerts with his rendering of 'Who is Sylvia, what is she?', while even the boss joined in with 'One Meat Ball'!

The scientific research covered a very wide field. Perhaps the most important section, under the direct control of Miss Davin, was concerned with breeding better flax varieties and was a continuation of research started at Lambeg in the early 1920s. This involved much examination of microscopic sections of flax stems, to determine by measurement the actual fibre content. There were also experimental plots nearby where the most promising lines could be propagated and the effects of different treatments tested. Flax-manuring trials carried out by the Ministry of Agriculture, with the produce being processed at West Newton, showed that neither

73

potash nor phosphate treatments were beneficial unless there was a marked deficiency of these compounds in the soil. There was also research on how to determine the right day for harvesting in relation to the maturation of the flax plant, so that the fibres have fully developed and the seed has set, but lignification of the stem has only just begun. A uniform moisture content throughout the plant seemed to be a useful indicator. Although in war-time very little of the flax crop was retted, because this antiquated process seemed unnecessary for production of the coarser fabrics most needed then, yet a rapid change-over was vital at the end of the war. So retting research had to go on although it proved very frustrating. This seemed to be because the process contained so many chemical and physical variables, especially in the retting liquor, that it proved impossible to correlate any known properties of the straw with its retting behaviour. The esoteric and noxious art of retting thus remained steeped in mystery. Moreover, the retting liquor was the only by-product of the whole flax industry which seemed to have no possible use. In one of his talks, Gilbert Searle suggested that it might be possible to market it in half-crown bottles for medicinal purposes:- 'It is full of salts and tastes just as bad as the accredited spa waters.'[1], but we suspect that he might have had his tongue in his cheek at the time. As an effluent it has a nasty smell and can pollute, so there is every incentive to reduce its volume. This is partly why the 'aerated ret' was invented by HMNFE scientists, since it meant that the same retting liquor was used over and over again and its total volume was much reduced. Large-scale experiments on chemical retting were also carried out at West Newton, with little success. A bigger and better commercial drier was also developed, which allowed the retted straw to be dried all the year round under controlled conditions. Eventually the retting complex was converted into research labs and offices for chemistry and physics.

The peak year of the war effort as far as flax production was concerned was 1944. About 62,000 acres were grown in England and Wales that year (5,662 acres of this in Norfolk, mostly around Sandringham), with a further 124,000 in Northern Ireland. Fibre needs of the Services increased also, especially for making parachute harness in this period of airborne troop movements: from 93,000 tons in 1943 to 124,000 in 1944[2]. Towards the end of 1944 a very heartening message came through from the General Officer commanding the Airborne Forces to everyone engaged in flax and linen production[3]: all the war-time needs of the Services for material derived from flax had been met in full - congratulations! This was quite an achievement for an enterprise which had started from a few acres grown on a Royal estate, but that small beginning had provided the catalyst from which all else followed.

As the light at the end of the tunnel grew brighter and a victorious end to the war became a near certainty, rather than just a hope, the likely future of the resuscitated flax industry was much discussed. Would it just wither away, as had happened after the 1914-18 War, or would it become a permanent feature of British agriculture? The Government's view, as expressed by the Department of Home Flax Production, seemed to be that it all depended on the growers. According to one spokesman, they would be given a couple of years in which to find out if flax could be produced at a cost which would justify State support[4]. Even before the end of the war some flax supplies were coming in from Belgium and Russia, so cheap imports from those sources would soon become a serious threat again. A different sort of threat was looming too, since new synthetic textiles were being developed which were bound eventually to compete with linen itself. So the prospective challenges of peace looked just as formidable as those of war. The question remained, could they be conquered too ?

When VE and VJ days came in 1945 the true extent of the linen industry's war effort could be gauged, in terms of the actual amounts produced of a range of essential items. According to the Flax Controller, these amounted to :-

26,500 miles of hose-pipe

20,000 miles of parachute webbing

54 million square yards of linen aeroplane fabric

25 million square yards of heavy canvas tarpaulins and hatch covers

75 million yards of 'blitz' fabric and linen dowlas

35 million yards of canvas and duck

9 million yards of scrim for packing and camouflage.

Millions of pounds weight of linen thread, twine, netting and various sorts of cordage were also produced[4]. It was indeed a gargantuan effort, which surpassed anything which could have been imagined when the war began in 1939.

Chapter 15. Peace at last: what it was like in the labs (JWT)

September 29th 1947 and a rather naïve school-leaver, not yet 16, started work at His Majesty's Norfolk Flax Establishment, Flitcham Abbey. Earlier that summer, I had cycled out to the factory for an interview for the job, and subject to a good School Certificate result, I was in. At that stage, I did not really know what I wanted to do, except that it should be something 'scientific', and a post in the plant pathology section seemed to meet the demand.

The establishment operated its own bus service, so all bright and shiny that Monday morning I started a routine that I was to follow for the next 7 years, changing buses at the factory for another that took us on to Flitcham. As with any new job, the first thing was to cover all the admin. demands, one of which was to sign the Official Secrets Act. 'Strong stuff this' I thought; a dramatic destiny beckoned, but after that, things did rather go downhill.

The plant pathology section was concerned with the biological factors that would influence satisfactory growth of the flax plant, and to that end, each year there would be local field trials. These would yield large quantities of flax from a wide range of plot experiments. The product from each plot had to be assessed initially by counting the number of straws in a measured sample, and then measuring individual straws. So my first 'scientific' job was counting and measuring flax straws! The bundles were fairly thick and numbered several hundred straws; the total number of bundles was endless, and I, along with other lowly members of staff, sat day after day counting and measuring. There was however a bonus: I had just come from a boys-only school, and now there were girls! More interesting work was going on at the same time, investigating seed-germination factors, fungal parasites and fungicidal treatment of seed, but for a long while I was only on the edge of that.

The staff at Flitcham was fairly small in number, and I soon got to know them. My head of department was Reg Goodman. I don't know how long he had been in flax, but his knowledge seemed limitless and he was an extremely busy man. His wife Marion was in charge of the office section. Reg's right-hand person was Marjorie Dodds, and they seemed to spend a great deal of time peering at seeds on agar culture plates and chanting a mantra that sounded like 'Phoma sp. Fusarium. Botrytis. Mucor.' These I found out were just some of the fungi that could infect flax. Pat Barrett, a local girl, spent much of her day using a noisy vacuum cleaner to pick up samples of 100 seeds and deposit them on damp blotting paper; it made percentage germination figures easy to calculate. Her father, Tom Barrett, was the lab. handyman and washer-up. My guide to all the short cuts was Allan Flowers. I had known him from school, although he was a year my senior. Within a week of my starting Pat Mummery joined the group; she too was fresh from school.

The other lab. at Flitcham was concerned with plant-breeding and headed by Dr A. G. Davin. She was one of the pioneers of English flax, having come over from Ireland in the '30s. At that time two local girls made up her team, Dorothy Sands from Flitcham, and Betty Hooks from Anmer. Betty had to cycle each day, not too bad in the morning, but going home at night up Flitcham hill must have been murder. She looked very fit.

Lunch was a culinary experience to be avoided if at all possible, but with rationing still in force it was not always possible. The food was prepared in the main canteen at the factory, packed into insulated containers, and transported up to us. It did not travel well. The statutory fish on Friday, packed in with the alternative macaroni cheese, was a particularly depressing way to end the week.

Being right on the edge of the known universe, the Abbey had its own power supply, maintained by Sonny Knight, the resident gardener. Whenever the demand on a bank of lead/acid accumulators exceeded the supply, a massive diesel-powered generator wheezed into life. You can well imagine that this finite supply of direct current posed several problems, particularly in the winter. At such times, when the demand was greater than the total capacity of the system, Sonny did not hesitate to speak his mind. On those occasions he could be very eloquent.

The local area obtained its water from a nearby natural source, and a subterranean ram lifted it up to a small tower. In later years I was to do a coliform bacteria count on this water. The results made me vow never to drink the stuff again, except in tea. I felt that nothing could live in Abbey tea.

November 1947 saw the wedding of Princess Elizabeth, and we were allowed to listen to the radio coverage. The solemnity of the occasion was marred however by the repeated playing of the National Anthem. Dr Davin insisted on standing up, indicating that we should do the same. After about half a dozen times however, we felt that national duty had been done and a 'bobbing up and down like this' situation developed. Dr D. was not amused.

Being based at Flitcham, there were many occasions when I had to go to the main factory. This gave me a good opportunity to find out how the other half lived, and my first impressions were of a hell on earth. The whole place was noisy, dusty and smelly: the noise of countless strange machines, the dust from various straw handling processes and the smell from the retting tanks. But it was amazing how quickly everything became commonplace and normal. Mind you, I was not at the cutting edge of industrial flax processing. Basically it always was a noisy dusty smelly way to earn a living, but I could usually walk away from it. This is exactly what had happened in earlier years during the war. Blackout conditions on the night shift demanded that all doors be shut. This created such bad working conditions that walk-outs did occur. By the time I got there, conditions, whilst not perfect, were at least tolerable.

December 1947 came and my first Christmas party at the factory. This was the age of 'Music Hall' and 'Workers' Playtime' on the radio, and the psychology of entertainment worked down to a local level, with various turns recruited from the employees. One that sticks in my mind was that of Miss Nolan. Miss Nolan was the Canteen Manageress. In today's terms she might have been referred to as 'vertically challenged', but what she lacked in stature she more than made up for in spirit. As far as I could tell, everyone feared Miss Nolan, and nobody argued with her, at least not twice. As I recall, her speciality was the piano-accordion, and her size 8 behind a full-sized accordion made it look as if the instrument was playing itself. It was not sophisticated entertainment, and the comedian's best laugh came from shouting out the name of the factory foreman, but it had a simple magic for me, and everyone went home happy.

The following spring my involvement with the first of many field trials began. These were a range of comparative experiments, and were designed to test the performance of seed varieties, and treatments to combat seed-borne fungi. Little was known at that time about many of the fungicides available for seed treatment. Many of them were organo-mercury based, and our crude methods of mixing seed with compound would warrant headline television coverage today. It was not until 2 or 3 years later that literature became available on the accumulative toxicity of organo-mercurial compounds. We had two large carboys of a product called Panogen, Swedish I think. I believe that in the end it had to be disposed of by methods used for chemical warfare materials[1]. The standard fungicide used in the factory was not based on such lethal foundations.

For the field trials, we hired 2 - 3 acres from a local farmer. The area was laid out in plots 8ft.(a drill width) by about 30ft and 3ft. paths in between. Sowing was a tedious process. Individual

Plots laid out for field trials, next to Paston's Clump

trials were replicated in various parts of the field and then the seed drill had to be totally cleaned out. This could be repeated a dozen or more times, and it was amazing how many times a pleasant mild spell before sowing was followed by a cold penetrating wind, just as we all had to work in the middle of a big field. Once the seeds started to germinate, the next stage was to kneel beside a plot, counting the number of seedlings within lft. squares. Oh the excitement of it all....but summer was coming! To keep the paths reasonably weed-free, we had a Trusty tractor. This is an engine on two wheels, with various hoeing or cultivating attachments bolted on. Steering was achieved by a crude clutch mechanism to either wheel. I was every sort of racing ace handling that beast. My arm still tingles when I think of the time someone turned the starting handle just as I was checking that the spark-plug lead was connected. Jolly good magnetos on Trusty tractors.

Whilst we were grubbing about in our own little microcosm, several sorts of organised chaos had been occurring in the real world. From the previous year, the fieldsmen had been negotiating with farmers, contracts drawn up, argued over and signed. Seed drills were dusted over and checked out, and vast quantities of seed made available. In Norfolk this might involve some 500 farmers contracting for nearly 6,000 acres. All this activity was not just local however. At its peak, the British flax industry operated something like 17 factories throughout England Scotland and Wales, with a total of 60,000 acres of flax being grown and processed. In 1947 the export of linen from British flax, was second only to Scotch whisky as a dollar-earner. I was getting £2.12s. 6d. a week!

So the summer progressed, and the plants grew. Then one morning, magic was in the air. The flax was in flower. I have never been able to find the right words to describe the glory of a flax field in full flower. A wash of blue that defies description, restless under a gentle breeze, creating an inland sea rolling across the countryside. The petals fall by mid-day, but the sequence is repeated with different plants for about a week. Present day linseed is pretty, but being short-stemmed it does tend just to stand about; in contrast, the long flax plants were alive with movement. With our variety trials, petal colours could be white or pink. This did rather break the poetry of the moment, but it was still delightful to see.

The critical days were now ahead. Because of its length (60-80 cms), as the seed heads developed the plant became top-heavy and unstable. Wet and windy weather at this stage would ground the plant, and greatly impair the next stage. The fibre within each stem went down to ground level, so cutting would have wasted a considerable amount. Instead, the plants had to be pulled out. This was done by pairs of inclined counter-rotating belts, the flax would be guided into the pinch of each pair of belts and whisked out and up into a sheaf-binder mechanism. Generally this system worked well until certain weeds were encountered. One particular brute, called 'fat hen', was fairly deep-rooted, very succulent and could be guaranteed to jump the belts off the wheels. The technique for replacing a belt would send a safety inspector of today into cardiac arrest. The tractor driver would engage the power take-up whilst someone kicked the belt back on with their foot! As the sheaves were ejected from the binder, so they were gathered up and stacked in a wigwam to dry. That was the theory; however, the realities of the weather often made it a very extended practice. The 'dry' sheaves were then loaded on to a trailer and hauled to the factory. There are many tales of the havoc wreaked by a large trailer of flax, on a small country road. Accident reports were forever being typed concerning lost pub signs, street-lights or even a bedroom window. I am told of one occasion when the load fell off (not an uncommon occurrence) and a car drove over some of the fallen bundles. The fibrous nature of the plant became so entangled with the prop-shaft, that major and costly surgery was necessary. The factory drivers tended to be pigeon-holed as to their characteristics ('speed-merchant', 'accident-prone', 'slow and careful') but they were a great

Some of the Lab. Staff and the gardener (A. Knight)
Back row, left to right: R. Borley, A. Knight, R. Goodman, P. Page, J. Drewry,
I. Hinch, E. Uren, M. Chalk.
Front row, left to right: P. Latter, B. Frowhawk, S. Edge,
K. Batterbee, B. Hooks

bunch of lads skilled in both Heavy Goods and Public Service vehicles. The vehicle maintenance shed was never dull.

The research labs. on the factory site at West Newton were concerned with production problems and, although I was a frequent visitor, I was not involved in much of the activity except the lunch-time pontoon schools. However, one of the senior staff - Ted Cox - will always be remembered. He was not an academic, but was one of the most practical and inventive characters I have ever known. The late '40s and early '50s were a time of shortages, so it was 'what have we got?' rather than 'what do we want?' Ted made his own car; it was a hybrid culled from the local scrapyards, but it worked and was legally taxed and insured. Just prior to the Coronation he made his own television set, a small screen with a green-hued picture, but it worked. I think his greatest triumph was growing his own tobacco. Cigarettes were in short supply, so one summer Ted grew some plants and set about curing the leaf. From what I heard however, a sharp attack of impatience prevented him from working the full cure. The resulting tobacco was far from Mr Players' finest. General opinion was that he might have had more socially acceptable results by smoking shive from the scutching turbines. I think that he had to obtain a licence for that particular venture. A licence was certainly needed for home-brewing, and he tried that as well.

Round about the turn of the decade, our department expanded. Two more lab. assistants joined: a local girl June Bennett, and a lad I had known at school, John Morley. John had an older brother Peter, and I had been in awe and envy of Peter. He could whistle through his teeth with such power that cars would slow down 200 yards away. Oh the ambitions of youth! Probably of greater value to the flax industry was the addition of Margaret Chalk and Pam Latter. At the same time Elspeth Uren joined the plant-breeding section, and she was to take this over when Dr. Davin retired.

Margaret and Pam were to expand the range of work in our department. The brief was to investigate the flora that contributed to the retting process in order to achieve higher fibre qualities. I was into my own laboratory research by now with various investigations into the mysteries of what went into making a good ret. The industrial process had long been established, but every so often a particularly good ret occurred. If the reasons could be isolated and duplicated, a significant advance would be made. This elusive goal had been the 'philosopher's stone' for many years, but I don't think the answer was ever found. There were too many variables involved and there could be little control over many of them. I did get my name on to a couple of papers however:- 'A bacterial study of flax retting' and 'Effects of temperature, dilution and aeration on the bacterial flora of retting liquor'. Nothing that was going to make the world of literature sit up and think, but it did my ego a power of good.

It was round about this time that the department got a new car. Our pre-war Hillman Minx had served us well, but it never really recovered from my blowing it up. This came about by another example of lateral thinking. We needed a 24-hour-a-day supply of compressed air for the aeration experiments. An electric compressor was out of the question with the Abbey power supply, so we got a large tractor-wheel, complete with tube and tyre, inflated it and coupled our demand to the slowly-leaking schrader valve. This was crude but fairly effective. The major shortcoming of the idea manifested itself, when one day, with the wheel in the back of the car, I was inflating the tyre from the M.V. shop compressor. Something distracted me from the matter in hand. I was returned to the moment by a massive explosion as the over-inflated tyre burst. Luckily the car doors were open, but even so, the sun roof was blown out and the interior fabric trim was reduced to cheap lace. My face remained red for quite a long while. Our new car was a new Ford Popular. It was typical of the range of lower cost cars of the early 50s and, whilst I can still remember the old Hillman (OMC 51) and its many foibles, all I can remember about the Popular is the smell of plastic, and that the foot-operated headlight dip-switch was so far to the left, that the passenger had to work it.

We now ran field trials in various parts of the country, in areas associated with some of the other flax factories. So from time to time Reg Goodman and I would take to the open road and head for such places as Uckfield, Crewkerne, Howden or Glemsford. Travelling by road in those days was much more pleasurable, the volume of traffic was low and progress was a gentle venture, for the most part.

By the time 1954 came along, I was getting restless, feeling the need to move on and hopefully up. The mood was heightened by rumours that the future of English flax was uncertain. As an established civil servant, job security was good but the pay scale was not. I looked into one or two posts in other areas of research, but in the end surrendered my soul to industry.

So, one bright Saturday morning in early May I departed Flitcham Abbey and H.M.N.F.E. It had been a good time, but the age of innocence was over and there were a lot of hills still to climb. It would be 10 years before I came back to live in West Norfolk again. 40 years on, and I go back from time to time and look round the factory site. Most of the buildings are still there, but it has been so long now that all the echoes have faded away, and even the ghosts have gone.

The young Jim Tuck

Chapter 16. Post-war struggles: the slow decline

When at last the war ended with the defeat of Japan as well as Germany the troubles of the British flax industry began. Naturally, the acreage sown was cut considerably because of the greatly reduced Service needs, so lower prices were set for the 1946 crop. This meant a surplus of good pedigree seed, so that large quantities could be sent to our newly-liberated allies on the continent: Belgium, France and Holland. Of course this allowed them, very quickly, to build up their flax and fibre production so that they could compete with Britain to supply the mills, indeed an ironic situation. To make matters worse, we had some special British difficulties because of our use of the 'green scutching' system in the war, which meant quicker processing yet was entirely adequate for what the Services needed, namely coarser fabrics. It took workers some time to adapt to the old method and achieve the fine fibre quality which was needed for making clothing and household linens.

Already in 1946 the Ministry of Supply decided to shut the Scottish factories[1], although one of them (Cupar) resisted and managed to continue for a while as a commercial concern independent of Government contracts[2]. At the same time, however, the Government guaranteed until 1948 an assured annual market for not less than 20,000 acres of English flax: only a third of the area grown in the later years of the war. Ulster's future acreage was left to be determined by price. The 1946 figure for England was actually set at 25,000 acres and the 1947 figure at 24,000.

In post-war years the stream of visitors to the flax factory at West Newton increased considerably, both in numbers and in their countries of origin. Most of those from overseas came from just across the Channel, especially from Belgium, France and the Netherlands. These flax-growing countries were naturally interested in British developments in the breeding and processing of this fibre. However, not all of them were impressed. Dr Robert Galley (who was in charge of the West Newton laboratories for a time) recalls the rather scathing remarks of some Belgian visitors to the effect

85

that they treated their flax as they treated their women: with great care. 'If you treat your women as you do your flax, then heaven help the women!' It is not altogether surprising that they felt their methods were superior, since Courtrai in Belgium was, and still is, an acknowledged centre of excellence in all things flaxen. Other visitors came from much further afield, e.g. Australia, New Zealand, Canada, Japan and even some African countries such as Egypt, Nigeria and Zululand. By 1954, numbers had dwindled again and the last visitor was recorded on February 3rd 1958, almost exactly 23 years after the first. Since the first recorded visitors were King George V and Queen Mary it was rather appropriate that the last was their grandson-in-law, Prince Philip, Duke of Edinburgh.

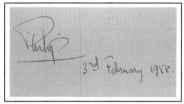

Relations between the Royals and the factory seem to have been reasonably cordial but there was at least one bone of contention[3]. This concerned the remarkably low rent for the 70-acre site. This was fixed in 1935 at £35 a year, with a 50-year lease. Already in 1943, when the scale of factory operations had increased considerably, the King (George VI) expressed some disquiet and asked to see the lease document. At first it could not be found, which doubtless caused some consternation. When it was, the King agreed the rent was fixed and could not be changed. However, his disquiet over the expansion of activities continued into peace-time and may have contributed to his decision not to advance money so that cottages for factory workers

The Flax Factory at its fullest extent (aerial view) in June 1958

86

could be built on the Royal Estate. This was a Government enterprise, he declared, so the Government should pay[4]. This awkward situation was eased in 1950 when the lease was transferred from the Ministry of Supply to the Board of Trade, which offered to increase the rent from £35 to £120, with a further increase in 1953. The King approved.

Botanical research, designed to produce improved flax varieties, continued in the labs at Flitcham Abbey until 1954. Dr Davin was in charge of this work until she left in 1952, when Miss E. M. Uren took over. The chief varieties produced in Norfolk were Norfolk Queen (high-yielding and immune to wilt), Norfolk Earl (with high fibre quality), Norfolk Princess (tall and wilt-resistant) and Norfolk Mandarin (tall, with very good fibre characteristics but easily flattened by bad weather). Norfolk Queen was blue-flowered, the rest purple[5]. Throughout this period selection was based mainly on the microscopic examination and measurements, of cross-sections of the stem in order to discover the percentage of fibre in it, since the Davin/Searle team had shown, back in 1920-21, that this percentage had high heritability, so could be selected for. The sections (3 per stem) were always cut half way between the cotyledon scar and the base of the first flowering branch on the stem. Sections from about 60,000 stems were examined during the course of this lengthy programme, spanning about thirty-four years. Plant height was another important variable because of its heritability, but the greater the height the greater the risk that the crop would be flattened by wind and rain.

Seed was saved from the most promising plants, sown thinly and bulked in subsequent generations. This would give up to one hundredweight of seed in five years from the single seed which produced the desirable plant. The performance of potential new varieties under field conditions was assessed. There were many other field trials which dealt with such factors as the effects of different fertilizers, of trace elements, fungicides and so on, as described in Chapter 15. Much of the lab-work at the West Newton factory during this early post-war period was concerned with the esoteric mysteries of retting. So many variables were involved that it is hardly surprising that no definitive formula for obtaining the perfect ret was ever discovered. The waters of the river Lys in Belgium, close to the town of Courtrai, continued to reign supreme.

Early in 1949, when Nathan Isaacs took over from Earl De La Warr as Director of Home Flax Production, the Board of Trade announced that the Home Flax scheme would continue at least until 1952[6]. By that year the area of flax grown in Great Britain had decreased to 16,000 acres, of which 1,750 were in Norfolk. Only ten of the original seventeen factories remained in production. It became increasingly clear that the Government (which changed from Labour to Conservative in 1951) wanted to withdraw completely from their flax-production and processing responsibilities and sell their interests to private enterprise. Bad weather in 1953 and 1954 accelerated the slide in production and showed how vulnerable the crop was to the vagaries of wind and rain. For instance, the *Northants Evening Telegraph* reported in July 1953 that soldiers from the local barracks were going to aid a force of over 200 men, women and children who were trying to save 2,200 acres of weatherbeaten flax from total ruin. Pulling machines could not tackle it in that state and £68,000 was at stake. The *Nottingham Guardian* told of a fight to save 1,500 acres flattened by wind and rain, with one grower touring farms and pubs to try and recruit a labour gang. The story was repeated in some districts in 1954, for instance in Northamptonshire, where it was reported that half the total crop might be lost through bad weather. These crises were not typical of the country as a whole but they show how weather could push up production costs to the point where they became uneconomic.

Lynn News & Advertiser

The King and Queen examine linen exhibits at the Royal Norfolk Show, Anmer, 1950

Princess Margaret looks at the flax exhibit

The last great opportunity to mount a splendid flax show came in June 1950, when the annual Royal Norfolk Agricultural Show was held in Anmer Park, which was part of the Royal Estate. The King, Queen and Princess Margaret were all there and spent some time in the large marquee devoted to the work of His Majesty's Norfolk Flax Establishment, with plenty of examples of beautiful end-products as well. This visit was the last (but not least) in their lengthy programme. At the end of the day 'the King appeared perfectly fresh'[7] but only a year and a half later he died in his sleep.

The young Tony Searle at Anmer, 1950

Chapter 17. Journey's end, with a final presentation

In 1953, the Home Flax Scheme lost £210,000, which increased to £500,000 in 1954. The production costs for British flax were then £500 a ton, compared with a world price of £200. It is not surprising that in August of that year the Government decided not to continue with the scheme beyond the 1955 harvest, when the Directorate of Home Flax Production was due to be wound up.[1] There were protests from the National Farmers' Union and much bitterness among the ten thousand workers in the industry, as well as at least one question in Parliament. In reply, the Government just quoted the loss of £300 a ton for flax produced under the scheme.

The situation worsened in 1956, when the Spinners' Association announced that if they were to sell linen on the world market they must buy flax fibre at world prices, which implied a 24% cut on the previous year's figures. From then on, the end was nigh. One by one the remaining factories closed down and the contents were sold for 'peanuts'. The last year that fibre flax was grown in the country on a commercial basis was 1955 and nearly all mills had closed by the end of 1957.

Lynn News & Advertiser

Gilbert Searle watches the final run

H.M.N.F.E. at West Newton was the last factory to close and continued to function until 1958. Processing of the final 1955 crop, which was a very large one, finished in February of that year. Appropriately, the last Sandringham crop ended up, like the first, as Royal linen. This time, however, only one firm, D. S. Honeyman Ltd. of Kirkcaldy, was involved (with its associates) and one particular person in the industry, namely R. Wemyss Honeyman. He was the same 'public-spirited individual' who had rescued Norfolk Flax at a critical time just before the war.

This valedictory presentation to the Queen was the brain-child of Gilbert Searle, who wrote to the Directorate of Home Flax Production on the subject in December 1955.[2] They showed no great enthusiasm for the idea, but agreed that 'some small gesture would not be altogether out of place', as long as it did not breach protocol and met with the Queen's approval. Nothing daunted, Major Searle seized the first opportunity to check the latter point. This came in January 1956, when he was invited to a New Year's party at Sandringham House where he had a chance to talk to the Queen and Queen Mother. Both told him how sorry they were that flax-growing on the Estate was coming to an end, whereupon Major Searle remarked that 'the last crop on the Estate looked like being one of the best.' The Queen then remarked that it would be nice to have some linen goods made from it as a souvenir; soon afterwards her genuine interest was confirmed. When approached, Mr Honeyman was delighted with the idea of obliging the Queen in this way, by taking over the whole Sandringham crop, spinning the flax thread at Messrs. N. and N. Lockhart of Kirkcaldy and then having it woven at the Honeyman mill and on the Jacquard looms of Erskine Beveridge of Dunfermline (a company of which Honeyman was Chairman). These were the same looms as were used to produce damasks for Balmoral Castle and Holyrood House in Edinburgh. He insisted that no cost would go to the Queen, while the Board of Trade obtained Treasury permission to chip in with £100 towards the total expense, which proved to be considerably more. By January 1957, Gilbert Searle could write to the Queen's Agent at Sandringham, Captain (later Sir William) Fellowes as follows:- 'Bearing in mind that our modest start in 1931 was solely due to the interest shown by King George V, and further that in 1939 it was the late King's powerful advocacy which led very fortunately to a wartime flax industry being set up, it would be a charming gesture if H.M. The Queen would graciously accept some linen, manufactured in Scotland from her own crop, as a memento of the twenty-five years' association.' Indeed, the Queen would do so, appreciating this 'most kind gesture' and expressing a special interest in sheets and pillow-cases. However, it was another couple of years before the whole consignment was ready for despatch to Sandringham, where it arrived on Jan. 7th 1959 for inspection by the Queen. It is not surprising that she was 'very pleased indeed' with it, since it contained not only linen sheets and pillow-cases (the former being truly Queen-size) but also twenty dozen damask table napkins, woven on the Jacquard looms and each embroidered with E.II.R. and 'Sandringham' underneath, as well as lots of kitchen cloths and some fine glass-cloths.

In the words of the Housekeeper at Sandringham, Mrs J. Robertson, it was 'a lovely gift'. Knowing the durability of linen, there seems little doubt that much of it is still in use today, forty years on. Unlike the presentation to King George V and Queen Mary in 1932, derived from the first Sandringham crop of 1931, there was no publicity for this final presentation. This was at the insistence of Mr Honeyman, who seems to have been a very modest man. Now, over forty years later, his generosity and his most effective help to the struggling 'Norfolk Flax Experiment' can surely be recognised. In Gilbert Searle's words after his own retirement:- 'I shall never forget your magnificent help in the early stages of the flax enterprise.'

The sad event which signalled the end of the Home Flax Scheme and of H.M. Norfolk Flax Establishment happened on March 12th-13th 1958. This was the sale by auction (and by order of the Board of Trade) of all the remaining plant, machinery, stores and equipment at the West Newton factory. Much of the scientific equipment, especially that at the Flitcham Abbey laboratory, had gone already to other Government research institutes. Much of the rest went for a fraction of its original value, mainly because this was

BUYERS MOVE IN ON MACHINES

TWO widely differing kinds of activity at the West Norfolk flax factory, machinery from which was auctioned yesterday and Wednesday. Top picture was taken on the last operating day before the factory closed down and shows Mrs. S. Bullock (left) of Grimston, and Mrs. W. Lawson, of Lynn, collecting the last flax from a scutching turbine, while the superintendent, Maj. C. O. Searle, looks on. Below, the same machine is being inspected by two prospective buyers shortly before the start of the auction. Story about the factory's closure appears on Page 17.

the last of the Government flax factories to survive. Only one buyer, from Belgium, may have been interested in the machinery from a functional aspect, rather than just as scrap metal. *Lynn News & Advertiser* Something had to be done too with all the research data.[3] As Searle wrote to Honeyman on March 7th 1958:- 'Our main research records have to be stored at the Public Records Depository, our very extensive card indexes at the Board of Trade library and our collection of photos at Kew.'

92

Files of correspondence etc. were nearly all burnt. Searle added that the whole place 'is now a shambles and I shall be glad to get away from it.' On April 1st he did, to start his retirement in Benenden, Kent. The 'Norfolk Flax Experiment' was over.

WHEATLEY KIRK PRICE

By Order of the Board of Trade (consequent upon closing down of the Home Flax Scheme).

Messrs.
WHEATLEY KIRK, PRICE & CO.
are instructed to offer for Sale by Auction (in Lots) on the premises,

on WEDNESDAY,
MARCH 12th, 1958, &
THE DAY FOLLOWING,
at 11 a.m. each day
The
PLANT, MACHINERY, STORES & EQUIPMENT
At H.M. NORFOLK FLAX ESTABLISHMENT, WEST NEWTON, KING'S LYNN.
comprising:—
A Scott 102in. x 98ft. Continuous Dryer; 4 Fairbairn Turbine Scutchers; B.U.S.M. De-Seeder; 2 Shakers; 2 Norfolk Tow Plants; Seed Cleaning Plants; Balers; Elevators and Conveyors; 15 Leterme and Boby Pullers; 2 Seed Drills; 14 Trailers; 15 Electric Pumps; Steel Tanks; Cochran No. 20 Steam Boiler, Dust Plants; 100 Electric Motors up to 25 h.p.; Steel and c.i. Piping and valves; 2 Trailer Fire Pumps; Weighing Machines; a Lang 18in. centres allgeared Lathe, 15ft. Bed; IXL 6in. Lathe; Town 42in. Radial Drill; Shaping Machine; Engineers Tools; Laboratory Instruments and Glassware; Office Furniture; Canteen Equipment and General Stores including Tyres; Machine and Electrical Spares.

Catalogues, when ready (price 6d.) from the Auctioneers, Messrs. Wheatley Kirk. Price and Co., 9 Rex Place, London, W.1. Tel: HYDe Park 8844.   C28.2K

FLAX FACTORY'S EQUIPMENT GOES

Auction at West Newton

THE LAST of the country's flax factories, that at West Newton, was the scene of a different kind of bustling activity on Wednesday and again yesterday.

Buyers from all parts of the country and one from Belgium inspected machinery and rows of implements before attending a large and varied auction at the factory's canteen. And yesterday saw the last of any major activity at H.M. Norfolk Flax Establishment, which closed recently by order of the Board of Trade.

Only a very few of the 200 or so buyers on Wednesday had any interest in the plant and machinery as such. For under the closing down of the Home Flax Scheme there are no remaining factories in this country. The Belgian buyer, who had interests in flax in his own country, was probably the only person interested for that reason.

Before the sale of Government departments some had already negotiated for the majority of the research and scientific equipment from the factory laboratory. Other departments from which lots were taken were the garage, tow barn, fibre store, scutching house, seed cleaning room, boiler and dryer houses, experimental retting room, implement shed and welfare room.

QUICK BIDS

Conducted by London auctioneers (Messrs. Wheatley Kirk, Price and Co.), bidding at the sale was swift. Among the buyers were local scrap metal merchants and private people wanting to pick up an odd article or two.

Indicative of the range of the auction were two lots side by side in the catalogue. One was of cupboards, which went for £1, and the other was a steam boiler, which sold for £350.

An amusing incident came

during the sale of a hot air dryer. After bidding had started at £10 and increased by £1s to £13, jumped to £60, one bidder took a £40 jump to £100 and was immediately ousted by his only rival with a bid of £150.

AFTER 30 YEARS

Watching buyers entering and leaving the sale room, the factory superintendent, Maj. G. O. Searle, who has been associated with the factory since its inception almost 30 years ago, remarked. "It is rather disappointing seeing it wound up."

Maj. Searle told our reporter that he would now be retiring, but would maintain an interest in flax by writing about it.

The factory had been closed, he said, for economic reasons. "I think the Government was right in closing it down." he said. "owing to the cost of flax fibre and the general competition from man-made fibres."

LAST CROP

Paradoxically, although the factory was closed as an economy measure, its last crop was the largest ever prepared by the factory. It totalled almost 4,000 tons.

Lynn News & Advertiser

Notices of the sale of the flax equipment

93

Chapter 18. Retrospect and future hopes

The history of British flax in the 20th century has been rather like that of a roller-coaster ride, but governed by national emergencies rather than gravity. Rather late in the Great War, at the time of the Russian revolution, its production shot unsteadily upwards because of desperate need. It hurtled down again soon after peace was declared, to reach rock-bottom during the Depression, when the global economy was in the same sad state. Then, thanks to the patriotic vision of a former Army officer (who hated to see this nation importing loads of the stuff when we could grow it perfectly well ourselves) coupled with the enthusiasm of our Monarch, it slowly started upwards again in a much more organized fashion. Fortunately this was at just the right time to allow it to play its vital role in fully satisfying enormous Allied demands in World War II, under the persuasive leadership of a gifted aristocrat. This was indeed 'its finest hour'! Thanks to continued Government protection in the post-war years its subsequent decline was gradual, but in 1958 all was over. Now, forty years on, only the skeleton of West Newton Flax Factory (and doubtless of others over the country) remains as a sad memento of a valiant effort to revive an age-old industry in this country. The question now arises, what can we hope for in the 21st century? Are there any signs of a flax revival?

The first point to note is that the flax plant, *Linum usitatissimum*, is still grown extensively in this country, but for its seed not its fibre: for linseed in fact. This is the same species as fibre flax, with the same lovely blue flower, but is a different variety. It is more branched and has a shorter stem, so it produces more seed but is less likely to be 'lodged' in bad weather. Apparently the introduction of 'set-aside' and other facets of the Common Agricultural Policy have made this quite a lucrative crop for farmers to grow[1]. After all, linseed makes very useful oil and a nutritious feed, with none of the complexities of pulling and scutching needed to obtain these end-products.

Quite recently, however, fibre flax too has been grown again in this country. This enterprise, by Robin Appel Ltd, began in collaboration with the Silsoe Research Institute and with financial aid from the Government[2]. Silsoe has developed a successor to the scutching machine, known as the Fibrelin decorticator, which separates the fibres from the woody part of the stem just like the former, after the flax straw has been 'dew-retted'. This involves spreading it out on the ground as a thin layer and letting it rot naturally by the action of bacteria and fungi. However, what is most novel about the flax-processing is that the flax plants are cut by a conventional combine harvester rather than being pulled by a special machine. This must greatly simplify the process but will also shorten the fibre lengths. Apparently this is not important for the products being made, which include non-woven fibres and linings for cars. It is interesting to note that another firm, Flax UK, part of the Gorham & Bateson group of companies, with headquarters in Downham Market, Norfolk, has opened a factory at Gayton, not far from West Newton. It is reported[3] that this will produce flax fibre for incorporation in the door panels of Mercedes and other cars. Apparently the flax fibre is blended with a small amount of plastic polymer fibre so as 'to get a more sustainable product and to make it bio-degradable.' So, once again Norfolk farmers will be growing fibre flax. They won't be pulling it, however, but either mowing it or using a combine harvester. Let's hope this new way of producing more environmental-friendly cars spreads far and wide among motor manufacturers. Clearly, fibre crops such as flax and hemp (and even nettles) can provide 'green alternatives' for a range of industrial processes, so prospects look bright.

In the 1980s and 90s there has been an encouraging resurgence in the demand for linen, particularly in garments and often blended with other fabrics, such as cotton, nylon and silk. In 1993 the *Drapers' Journal* described linen as 'the summer fabric of the 1990s'. International fashion designers frequently include it in their latest collections, to which it seems to add a certain cachet which no other fabric can, except possibly silk. Moreover, linen garments nowadays are 'far more crease-resistant than linen of old', with a natural look which is ideal for a week-end in the country.[4]

We seem to be moving out of a 'plastic civilisation' into one in which natural fibres are once more held in high esteem. This is reflected in the marked revival of fibre flax growing in Western

Europe, especially in France, Belgium and the Netherlands. Courtrai in Belgium is still the centre of the world flax market, with its high concentration of flax merchants and brokers, and with the latest and most sophisticated flax machinery on sale. Much flax is also grown in Poland and doubtless in other East European countries. Dutch and Polish varieties are sown there; regrettably we have found no evidence for the use of Liral or Norfolk pedigree seed anywhere. Methods used to process flax for fibre seem to have changed little. Pulling and deseeding are a combined operation, which is usually followed by dew-retting, which is much more economical (and less smelly) than other methods. Scutching, swingling or decorticating machines (take your pick as to name) are probably more sophisticated than in the 1940s and almost certainly produce less dust, but plenty of shives. These are regarded as an important by-product, being converted into boards for the furniture industry. Much research is still going on, some of it in the United Kingdom, to investigate different aspects of flax and its processing, from the properties of flax fibres to pests and weed control, even more studies on retting. Genetic engineering methods are replacing plant-breeding in attempts to produce a superior type of flax plant.

So much for the rest of Europe. As far as this country is concerned, we have seen some signs of a rebirth in fibre flax production but in an unexpected direction: car panels rather than damask tablecloths. However, the spinners and weavers are still there in Northern Ireland, so once the economic conditions are suitable and the right sort of machinery available then maybe some modern equivalent of George V will get things going again here (unfortunately without the help of LIRA, which exists no longer). Linen has been truly described as 'old as the hills but modern as the hour.' It has survived for many millennia and will remain for many more.

Notes and References

Introduction

1. Morshead, O. (1949) George V (1865-1936) *Dictionary of National Biography*, 1931-1940, pp.313-334.
2. Linnaeus, C. (1753) *Systema Naturae*, 10th edition.
3. *Leaves from Gerard's Herball,* arranged by Marcus Woodward, London, Thorson's, 1972.
4. From Cornish Linen Service Group web-site, found beside that for Ferguson's Irish linen, one of the firms which produced real linen articles for the presentation to George V.
5. Article on 'Irish Linen - nature's miracle fabric' in *The Times*, Nov. 28th, 1966.

Chapter 1

1. This magnificent 12th century font is made of black Tournai marble, with a different biblical scene carved on each of the four sides. It is fully described in the Church guidebook.
2. From *A History of Technology, vol. 1*, Oxford, Clarendon Press, 1985. See also *Flax and Linen* by Patricia Baines. Princes Risborough, Shire Publications, 1985.
3. See *Egyptian Textiles* by Rosalind Hall. Princes Risborough, Shire Publications, 1986. This book is a mine of information on the uses of linen in Ancient Egypt.
4. The dress concerned is exhibited in the Petrie Museum at University College London.
5. From the collection of Gilbert Searle, probably from tombs at Beni Hasan. Much of the historical information given in chapters 1 and 2 is from a lecture he gave at the Belfast Municipal Museum on 13th December 1933. We regret we could not always locate sources.
6. Article on 'Tax forms find revises history of writing', in *The Guardian* for Dec. 16th 1998.
7. Book of Exodus, chapter 39, verses 27-29. The Holy Bible. Oxford University Press.
8. Book of Proverbs, chapter 31, verses 13, 19, 24.
9. Gospel according to St. Mark, chapter 15, part of verse 46.

Chapter 2

1. See *Extracts from Ancient and Modern Writers on the Flax Crop*, by John Warnes. London, Edwards and Hughes, 1844.

2. Young, Arthur (1776) *The State of Ireland*.

3. Article by Michael Harrison entitled 'Ulster owes him her prosperity', *Everybody*'s magazine, Aug. 5th, 1950.

4. See Chapter IV of *Bound to the Soil - Social History of Dorset, 1750-1918,* by Barbara Keir. John Barker, London, 1968 and Dorset Books, 1993.

5. See the official guide to St. George's Chapel, Windsor Castle (published by Jarrold, Norwich) which illustrates a brake surrounded by a garter. This implement is called a 'hemp-bray' in the guide, but its proper name seems to be 'brake' rather than 'bray' (*Oxford English Dictionary*). Hemp was grown all over Britain but could only be used to make coarse fabrics; probably this tool could tackle both species of fibre-producing plant. Sir Reginald Bray's Chantry is now used as a shop!

6. Searle, G.O. (1936) 'A report on progress towards an organized British flax industry'. 173pp., unpublished Ms.

7. See LIRA Memoir no. 153 by M.K.E. Allen.

8. Letter from Sir Ernest Herdman in the Belfast News-letter on April 13th 1946. His father was a member of the committee which planned the flax exhibition, so, as the writer adds, the story can't be entirely dismissed although it can't be proved.

Chapter 3

1. See *Reasons for the cultivation of Flax in Great Britain and Ireland, or A Voice for the Poor* by John Warnes. London, Edwards and Hughes, 1843.

2. Searle, G.O. (1936) 'The past and future of flax production in Great Britain'. Proceedings of the Textile Institute Conference, London, 1936.

3. From ref. 6 of chapter 2.

4. Searle, G.O. (1959) Flax in Great Britain: technical developments from 1939 to 1957. Unpublished Ms.

Chapter 4.

1. Curtiss, J.C. (1919) *Scientific research for the linen trade*. Belfast, Wm. Strain and Sons. This comprises a reprint of articles written for the Provisional Research Committee, with introduction by Sir Edward Carson.

2. Linen Industry Research Association (1921) Report of the Council, 1920. Belfast, W. and G. Baird (Printers).

Chapter 5.

1. Pearson, K. and Davin, A.G. (1921) 'On the sesamoids of the knee-joint, Parts I and II'. *Biometrika* 13: 133-175 and 350-400.

2. Pearson, K. and Davin, A.G. (1924) 'On the biometric constants of the human skull'. *Biometrika* 16: 328-363.
3. Searle, G.O. and Davin, A.G. (1922) 'A botanical study of the flax plant. I. The application of statistical methods to plant selection work with flax'. LIRA Memoir no. 4.
4. Davin, A.G. and Searle, G.O. (1925) 'A botanical study of the flax plant. IV. The inheritance and inter-relationships of the principal plant characters'. *J. Textile Inst.* 16: T61-T82.
5. Gibson, W.H. (1931) Flax wax and its extraction. *Trans. Inst. Chem. Engineers* 9: 30-35.
6. Gibson, W.H. (1936) The separation of flax fibres from the plant stem. Proceedings of the Textile Institute Conference, London, 1936. See also Chap. 3, ref. 2.

Chapter 6
1. Searle, G.O. (1929) 'Old wine in a new bottle: flax as a hope for British agriculture'. (Written for publication in the *Daily Mail*)
2. *The Times*, Jan. 23rd, 1931.
3. *The Times*, Feb. 13th, 1931.
4. *The Times*, Nov. 25th, 1930.

Chapter 7
1. The Landmark Trust Handbook, 17th edition, with foreword by the Prince of Wales, was published in 1998. The Trust's address is Shottesbrooke, Maidenhead, Berkshire SL6 3SW.
2. Full report in the Belfast News-letter, Dec. 20th 1932; also in *The Times* for Dec 20th and 21st.
3. *The Times*, July 28th, 1932.
4. Searle, G.O. (1932) 'Flax for the linen industry'. Leaflet published by the Linen Industry Research Association in July 1932.
5. Searle, G.O. (1932) 'Proposals for the establishment of a flax industry on the Sandringham Estate'. From Royal Archives, Windsor Castle, ref. RA PP Sandringham 308.
6. Letter from Sir Frederick Ponsonby to Mr A.C. Beck, dated Aug. 25th 1932. From Royal Archives, Windsor Castle, ref. RA PP Sandringham 308.
7. Letter of Aug. 10th 1932 from G.O. Searle to R.E. Harwood in reply to letter of Aug. 9th to W.H. Gibson which contained various questions from the King on financial and other aspects of growing flax. Royal Archives, Windsor Castle, ref. RA PP Sandringham 308.
8. Despatch of press cuttings on Sandringham Show to Royal Yacht. Royal Archives, ref. RA PP Sandringham 308.

Chapter 8
1. Letter from R.E. Harwood to A.C. Beck, December 1933, about the delay in a decision to erect flax factory. Royal Archives, ref. RA PP Sandringham 308.
2. Letter from W.H. Gibson to R.E. Harwood , December 1933, on attitude of Flax and Fibre Production Committee. Royal Archives, ref. RA PP Sandringham 308.
3. *The Times* article of Feb 5th, 1935 on 'The King's Flax: Royal visit to Factory. Success of Sandringham Experiment.', with pictures.
4. Farson, Daniel (1982) Henry, an appreciation of Henry Williamson. London, Michael Joseph.
5. It is in his Foreword to the *Flax of Dream* (London, Faber and Faber, 1936), described as a novel in four books, that Williamson salutes Hitler as a 'great man...whose life symbol is the happy child.' He learned too late how terribly wrong he was. HW was one of the young Searle's heroes because of his nature writings and he was thrilled to meet him by chance in Norwich in 1940 when both were at an agricultural course. Lady Downe appears in his *The Story of a Norfolk Farm* as Lady Sunne.
6. Williamson, Anne (1995) *Henry Williamson, Tarka and The Last Romantic.* Stroud, Alan Sutton.
7. Royal Archives, ref. RA PP Sandringham 308.

Chapter 9
1. Ziegler, P. (1990) King Edward VIII, the Official Biography. London, Collins.
2. Windsor, Edward, Duke of (1960) *A King's Story.* London, Cassell.
3. Vickers, H. (1995) *The private world of the Duke and Duchess of Windsor.* London, Harrods. This contains snapshots of the King at Felixstowe and at the shooting-party.
4. Donaldson, F. (1974) *Edward VIII.* London, Weidenfeld and Nicholson. See also Michael Bloch's account of *The reign and abdication of Edward VIII.* London, Bantam Press, 1990.
5. *The Times,* Oct. 20th 1936: 'The King in Norfolk.'
6. Mott-Radclyffe, Charles (1971) Biography of Sir Samuel Hoare (Lord Templewood). *Dictionary of National Biography* (1951-1960), 487-490.
7. *Lynn News,* Oct. 23rd 1936.

Chapter 11
1. Document on 'The Norfolk Flax Experiment' by G.O. Searle. Royal Archives, Windsor Castle, ref. RA PP Sandringham 308.

Chapter 12

1. See chapter 3, ref. 4. The twelve new mills were at Cupar in Fife, Turriff in Aberdeenshire, Crewkerne in Somerset, Uckfield in Sussex, Glemsford in Suffolk, Devizes in Wiltshire, Milford Haven in Pembrokeshire, Howden in East Riding, Easingwold in Yorkshire, Newark-on-Trent, Cambridge and Lincoln.
2. Durst, D. (1980) 'Norfolk flax'. *J. Norfolk Industrial Society.* 2: 37-44.
3. Searle, G.O. (1946) 'Research in the flax industry'. *Ann. Applied Biol.* 33: 326-331.
4. *The Times*, April 6th 1943.
5. *The Times*, July 10th 1943.
6. *The Farmers' Weekly*, April 9th 1943 and in many other newspapers.
7. MacMillan *Dictionary of Women's Biography,* ed. Jennifer Uglow. 2nd edition, 1989. London, MacMillan.
8. *Who was Who*, vol. VI, 1961-1970. London, Adam and Charles Black.

Chapter 13

1. Selkirk, G.N.D.-H. (1986) Earl De La Warr (1900-1976). *Dictionary of National Biography,* 1971-1980, pp.752-753.
2. *Sussex Express*, Feb. 19th 1943.
3. *Belfast Newsletter*, June 11th 1942.
4. *Somerset County Gazette*, Oct. 23rd 1943.
5. *Yorkshire Post*, Nov. 23rd 1943.
6. *Yorkshire Gazette*, Oct. 1st 1943 (and in many other newspapers).

Chapter 14

1. See chap. 12, ref. 3
2. Barber, W.E. (1944) 'Flax-growing in England'. *Country Life*, Nov. 3rd.
3. *Hull and Yorkshire Times*, Nov. 25th 1944.
4. Caldwell, S.A.G. 'The linen industry'. *Textile Weekly*, Feb 15th.

Chapter 15

1. Details were released in 1995 (see *Guardian* of March 28th) of Operation Sandcastle (1954-56) in which more than 71,000 'bombs' containing nerve-gases etc. were loaded on to ships, which were then scuttled in the Irish Sea. Included in one consignment were 'some 50 strong containers of toxic seed dressings from H.M. Norfolk Flax Establishment'. Doubtless these included the toxic fungicides mentioned by Jim Tuck.

Chapter 16

1. *Statist*, Feb. 9th 1946 on 'Post-war flax policy.'
2. *Textile Weekly*, March 8th 1946
3. Correspondence of Ulick Alexander, Feb. 1943. Royal Archives, Windsor Castle, reference RA PP Sandringham 308.
4. Alexander to W.A. Fellowes, Oct. 1945. Royal Archives, Windsor Castle, ref. RA PP Sandringham 308.
5. Gilling, D.R. (1990) Flax in Norfolk. Also 'Flax breeding and bulking, 1911-1954' by G.O. Searle (unpublished spreadsheet).
6. *The Farmers' Weekly*, March 11th 1949.

Chapter 17

1. Judging from correspondence with G.O. Searle it was still operational in late 1957.
2. All the information on this presentation is from Gilbert Searle's dossier of correspondence etc. entitled 'The Queen's Linen'.
3. In a lengthy memorandum dated October 28th 1954 Searle laid out detailed plans for the publication (preferably by the Stationery Office) of 'a full account of the Establishment's work, particularly on the research side'. This would be based mainly on 'the 632 Flax Committee papers' and would be a collaborative effort between staff members, with one or more chapters or parts of chapters being contributed by E.G. Cox, R.L. Freeman-Taylor, D.R. Gilling, R.E.J. Goodman, C. Manley, L.J. Rhodes, G.O. Searle and Miss E.M. Uren. Searle would act as Editor-in-Chief and the final draft should be ready by April 1st 1955. Picking All Fool's Day for its completion was asking for trouble. Indeed, there was really no hope of all the sections being completed in a mere five months; nor, indeed, were they ever completed, apart, it seems, from a few, mainly by Searle himself. After his retirement he agreed with a publisher to prepare an authoritative monograph on flax, but regrettably it failed to materialise before his death in 1968.

Chapter 18

1. Whitlock, R. (1992) 'The rolling flaxen acres'. *Guardian Weekly*, Aug. 16th.
2. See video by Robin Appel Ltd (01489 896388) entitled 'Fibre Flax, the path to profitable production.'
3. Skinner, Sue (1998) A piece of Norfolk in a flagship German car. *Eastern Daily Press*, Feb. 19th.
4. Craik, Laura (1999) 'Doing what comes naturally', *The Guardian* April 14th.

Index